3

the coming of age

1 — Recent Changes in Care Services

Significant changes in the care system have made it difficult to meet increasing demands from an ageing population.

2 — Assessing and Arranging Care

Better procedures need to be agreed in order to improve the services and choices for older people.

3 — Rebalancing Services

The NHS and social services must devise new initiatives together to ease the pressures that both are facing.

4 — The Way Forward

Short- and medium-term actions are required at a number of levels.

UNITED KINGDOM Audit Com.

CL

WT 27   9707624

Contents

© Audit Commission 1997

First published in October 1997 by the Audit Commission for Local Authorities and the National Health Service in England and Wales, 1 Vincent Square, London SW1P 2PN

Printed in the UK for the Audit Commission by Kent Litho

ISBN 1 86240 059 8

Photographs: Paul Baldesare/Photofusion (p83), Garth Blore (p60), Sally and Richard Greenhill (Cover, pp27, 39, 71, 78), Sally Lancaster (p37), Brenda Prince/Format (p5), Hilary Shedel (pp17, 21), Tony Sleep (p81), Christa Stadtler/Photofusion (p47), Telegraph Colour Library (p3), Neil Walker (p30).

Illustration: Fred Van Deelen, p51

Preface

The Audit Commission oversees the external audit of local authorities and the National Health Service (NHS) agencies in England and Wales. As part of this function the Commission is required to undertake studies to enable it to make recommendations for improving the economy, efficiency and effectiveness of services provided by these bodies; and it is required to comment on the effects of statutory provisions or guidance by central government on the economy, efficiency and effectiveness of these agencies.

Over the last 15 months the Commission has conducted two related studies in the field of care services:

- continuing care – a review of the arrangements for people leaving hospital who require ongoing or 'continuing' care; and

- commissioning of community care – a review of how local authorities commission services for those who are assessed as needing care.

Both studies had a focus on the care of older people (typically those aged 75 plus) and the results have therefore been combined in this report to make recommendations to those involved in delivering these services and those responsible for policy. Drawing from this research base the report comments on a complex, multi-agency service at a time of considerable national interest in care of older people.

The combined studies of care of older people follow the series of community care bulletins and reviews of services for older people with hip fracture, as well as general studies of the NHS [EXHIBIT 1, overleaf]. Future studies by the Commission will include a review of the role of housing in community care, rehabilitation services and district nursing services.

The studies on which this report is based were carried out by Stuart Turnock, Laura Hawksworth, Caroline Powell, Chris Baker and Maggie Kemmner of the Health and Social Services studies directorate of the Commission under the direction of David Browning and Jonathan Boyce. Fieldwork for the report took place in twelve local authorities, health authorities and associated trusts in England and Wales. Extensive consultation with independent providers was also conducted through fieldwork, meeting with associations and through representation on the advisory group (see Appendix 2): their help is appreciated. The team was assisted by the expert advice of Dr Michael Whitelaw, consultant geriatrician. Amanda Hale helped with the data analysis.

EXHIBIT 1

Related reports by the Audit Commission

A number of related pieces of work have been published recently and are planned for the future.

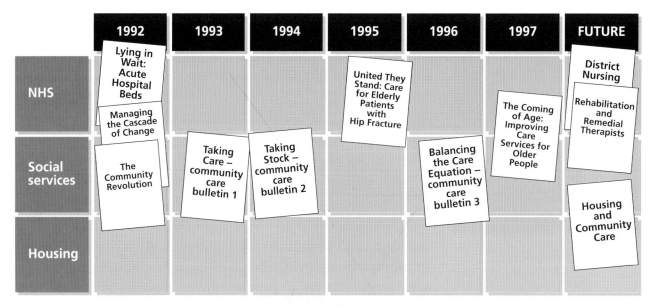

Source: Audit Commission

1

Recent Changes in Care Services

An ageing population is placing increasing demands on the
NHS and social services for long-term care. Unplanned
changes that occurred during the 1980s have left a legacy
that is still posing challenges for those involved.

EXHIBIT 2

Survival rates through the ages

The chances of someone living beyond the age of 75 are better now than they have ever been.

Percentage surviving

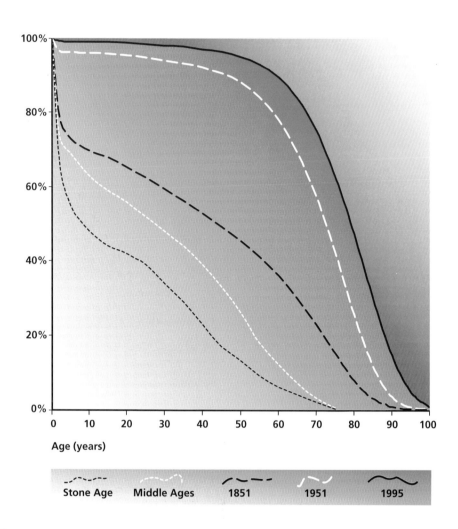

Age (years)

Stone Age   Middle Ages   1851   1951   1995

Source: OPCS; Government Actuarial Service

1. More and more people in this country are surviving to old age. The chances of someone living beyond the age of 75 are better now than they have ever been [**EXHIBIT 2**].

2. Increasing longevity is one of the greatest achievements of the twentieth century. But it is rarely recognised as such: all too often it is regarded as a problem rather than an achievement. This is because longevity on its own is not enough. It must be accompanied by adequate finances, fitness and good health so that quality of life is maintained for both older people and their families. Maintaining good health requires active care, preventing ill-health wherever possible, providing active rehabilitation after illness, and getting the right kind of support where health is failing. These measures, in turn, require careful planning and investment to ensure that the resources needed are in place to promote the well-being of older people.

Services for older people

3. The public sector is a major provider of services for older people [EXHIBIT 3]. These services include those that help to:

- prevent ill-health occurring in the first place, including those designed specifically to do so, such as primary care that provides checks and advice (GPs and community nurses); and those designed for other purposes from which any health gain is secondary, such as leisure and transport that help older people to keep fit and active, and housing that provides them with a warm and safe environment;

- treat ill-health when it occurs, through primary care services and in hospitals;

- promote recovery afterwards: for example, by active rehabilitation (usually involving physiotherapists and occupational therapists and others) both in hospital and in people's own homes; and

- provide social and healthcare on a continuing basis where full recovery is not possible, either in people's own homes (in the form of community nursing, home care, day services and others) or in alternative accommodation (such as sheltered housing or residential or nursing homes).

Together, all these services provide a wide range of support.

EXHIBIT 3

Services that help older people

Together, all these services provide a wide range of support.

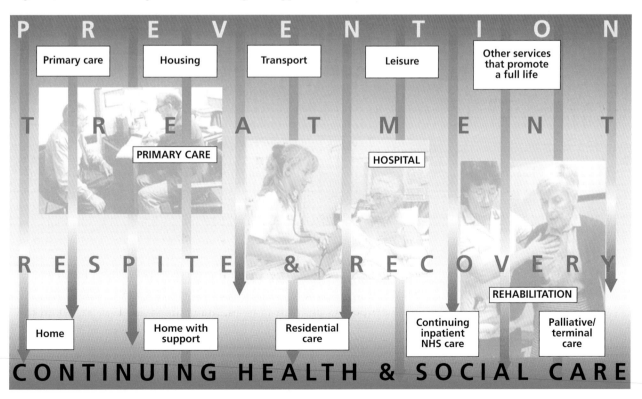

Source: Audit Commission

4. Many of these services interact, although usually in ways that are complex, poorly understood and rarely quantified. In theory, these interactions should make it possible to enhance value for money by substituting services that have a better outcome per pound spent for less cost-effective services. For example, increasing rehabilitation treatment in hospitals may make it possible for more people to return home with moderate amounts of home care rather than move to more expensive care in residential or nursing homes, although the circumstances in which this becomes possible and cost-effective are not easy to specify. Conversely, gaps and reductions in one service sector may put undue pressure on others. The situation is made more complicated by the range of different agencies involved, including the National Health Service (NHS) and local authority social services departments which provide or co-ordinate much of the social care, increasingly with independent sector providers.[1]

Longevity and use of care services

5. The need to review the adequacy of services for older people is becoming more pressing as demographic trends continue to change the underlying structure of the population. The projected future growth in numbers of older people has been well publicised. In fact, the age structure of the United Kingdom (UK) has already changed remarkably. For example, between 1981 and 1997, the total population increased by just 5 per cent, but while there was a drop in those aged between 65 and 74, those aged between 75 and 84 increased by 18 per cent, and those over 85 increased by 80 per cent [EXHIBIT 4] (Ref. 1). The growth in the numbers of older people in the period up to 2011 will continue but at a slower pace, allowing some time to plan. But growth in the numbers of elderly people is then projected to accelerate in the period after 2020.

6. These trends have significant resource implications. Nationally, those aged over 65 constitute 14 per cent of the population but account for 47 per cent of Department of Health (DoH) expenditure (Ref. 2), and 48 per cent (Ref. 3) of local authority social services expenditure. Two-thirds of admissions to the specialty of general medicine (including geriatric medicine, which overlaps general medicine) are of people aged 65 years or over (Ref. 4).

7. But it is the increasing numbers of people aged over 75, and especially over 85, which are putting the greatest pressures on services, both because they are increasing in number more rapidly and because their use of services is proportionately greater [EXHIBIT 5]. Wherever possible, statistics in this report refer to these older age groups.

I   Private and voluntary sector service providers.

EXHIBIT 4

Demographic changes since 1981 and over the next 80 years

Demographic trends are changing the underlying structure of the population.

Source: ONS Population Estimates, ONS Series 2, No. 20, 1994; Government Actuarial Service

Age group populations expressed as a percentage of their 1981 levels

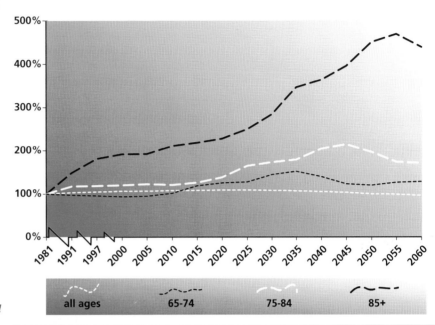

| all ages | 65-74 | 75-84 | 85+ |

EXHIBIT 5

Use of main care services by age group, England, 1996

People aged over 75, and especially those over 85, are putting the greatest pressures on services.

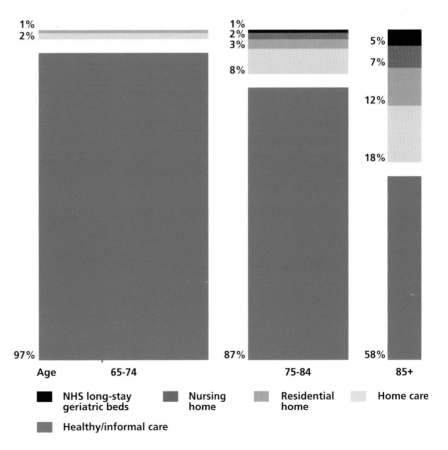

- NHS long-stay geriatric beds
- Nursing home
- Residential home
- Home care
- Healthy/informal care

Notes: Percentages of each age group: area represents relative size of age group.
Excludes home care organised outside social services departments and community health services.

Source: Care of Elderly People Market Survey, Laing & Buisson, 1997; DSS; DoH

Recent changes in service provision

8. The growth in the number of people aged over 75 and 85 over the last few years has been taking place at a time of significant change in the way that continuing health and social care – the bottom of Exhibit 3 – are provided and funded. These changes, and the way in which services have responded to them, are the subject of this report.

9. Prior to 1983, most publicly funded care was provided directly by the public sector – either through the NHS (acute care, community health, and long-term beds), or by local authorities through social services (residential, day and home care) and housing departments (housing with support). In the early 1980s, social security payments became available to pay for care in private and voluntary sector residential and nursing homes (but not for day or home care) of anyone qualifying for supplementary benefit, irrespective of need (Ref. 5). These payments were not cash-limited in any way and provided an injection of extra funds that rose steadily to £2.5 billion per year by 1993, which in turn funded the care of the increased numbers of older people.

10. But these extra funds were channelled entirely into residential and nursing home care and were not available for other services. Not surprisingly, this led to a rapid expansion of the residential and nursing home market throughout the 1980s, with independent sector nursing and residential beds increasing by 242 per cent from 1983 to 1996 **[EXHIBIT 6]**. Over the same period, the total number of places in residential accommodation in the independent sector in the UK rose by 124 per cent; by contrast, the number of local authority residential beds fell by 43 per cent (Ref. 6).

EXHIBIT 6

Residential and nursing home beds in the UK for the elderly and physically disabled

There was a rapid expansion of the residential and nursing home market throughout the 1980s.

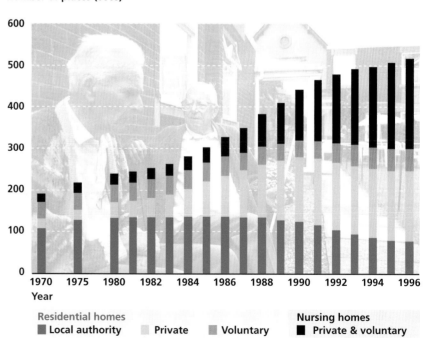

Number of places (000s)

Residential homes
- Local authority
- Private
- Voluntary

Nursing homes
- Private & voluntary

Source: Care of Elderly People Market Survey, Laing & Buisson, 1997

A key objective was to increase flexibility and ensure greater choice...

11. According to one commentator, the 'availability of social security payments for residential and nursing home care fuelled growth in such services at levels significantly greater than that necessary to keep pace with demographic pressures: by 1991, the number of older people living in long-term care establishments was 27 per cent greater than would have been the case if age-related levels of provision had remained constant since 1981' (Ref. 7). At the same time, as demand for expensive care in residential and nursing homes soared, the provision of home care failed to keep pace with the growing population. Between 1977/78 and 1984/85, provision of home care hours per head aged 75 plus provided by local authorities fell by 15 per cent (Ref. 8), with a further 10 per cent fall between 1986/87 and 1992/93 (Ref. 9). Thus, throughout the 1980s, residential and nursing home care expanded while home care reduced per head of population aged 75 plus.

12. This trend was brought to an end when the NHS and Community Care Act was enacted in 1990 and introduced on 1 April 1993. Under the provisions of this Act, local authority social services departments became the lead agencies for arranging social care. The additional funds made available through the social security system were capped and transferred to local authorities through the special transitional grant (STG) in addition to their standard spending assessment (SSA) **[EXHIBIT 7]**. A key objective was to increase flexibility and ensure greater choice between the types of care available: the grant was available for home care as well as for care in residential and nursing homes.

EXHIBIT 7

Resources made available for social services in England by central government

As a result of the NHS and Community Care Act, the additional funds made available through the social security system were capped and transferred to local authorities through the special transitional grant.

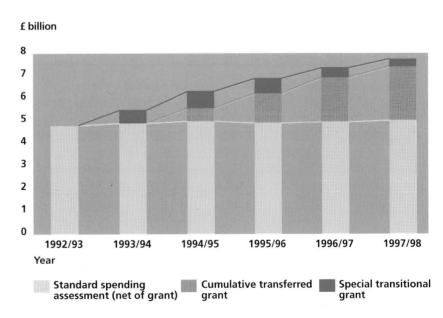

£ billion

Legend: Standard spending assessment (net of grant) — Cumulative transferred grant — Special transitional grant

Source: DoH

13. But the changes of the 1980s left two further legacies:

- a reduction in the role of the NHS; and
- a growth in the role of the independent sector.

Neither of these changes was planned; they happened by default as a direct result of the increase in social security payments. They represent major shifts in policy that have never been debated or agreed. They are considered in turn below.

Change in the provision of NHS care

14. The availability of social security monies in the 1980s enabled many health authorities to reduce their own provision for long-term care, closing old, outdated geriatric and psychogeriatric wards, and freeing the revenue for use elsewhere. Between 1983 and 1996, there was a 38 per cent reduction in acute and long-stay beds for older people and an almost ninefold increase in nursing home beds [**EXHIBIT 8**]. While a small proportion of nursing home places is purchased by health authorities – 8 per cent in 1996 (Ref. 6) – most are funded from other sources. As the House of Commons Health Committee stated, this 'has gradually created a situation in which general, as distinct from specialist, long-term nursing care is no longer considered to be an NHS responsibility but rather as social care and thus eligible for means testing' (Ref. 11).

EXHIBIT 8

Changes in continuing healthcare provision in England

There was a 38 per cent reduction in beds designated for older people and an almost ninefold increase in nursing home beds.

Beds (000s)

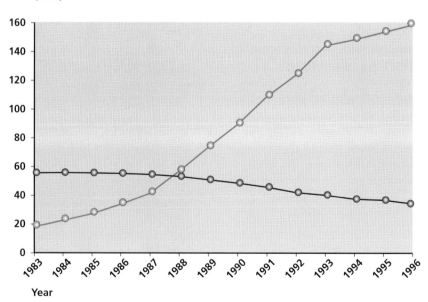

Year

—○— NHS beds in elderly (general) wards   —○— Independent sector nursing homes

Source: 1983-1994: House of Commons Health Committee (Ref. 10); 1995/96: DoH, Nursing Homes and Private Clinics Bulletin (1996 and 1997 issues) and Bed Availability for England (financial years 1994/95 and 1995/96)

...these changes... represent major shifts in policy that have never been debated or agreed.

15. In effect, the NHS has increasingly narrowed its role to that of a provider of acute care. This shift has not, however, gone unchallenged: in January 1994 the Health Service Commissioner reported on the investigation into a complaint on behalf of a woman whose husband, suffering from severe brain damage, was discharged to a private nursing home when he no longer needed acute hospital care. Her complaint was that she had been placed under an obligation to pay for long-term or 'continuing' care which should have been provided free of charge by Leeds Health Authority. The Health Service Commissioner upheld the complaint. Both the then Minister of Health and the NHS Chief Executive told the House of Commons Health Committee that the NHS had withdrawn too far from its responsibilities in relation to continuing care (Ref. 11).

16. In response to the concerns expressed in the Commissioner's report, the DoH issued guidance in February 1995 on NHS responsibilities for meeting continuing healthcare needs which called for reinvestment in many areas (Ref. 12). It required health authorities to develop local policies and criteria to serve as the basis for decisions in individual cases about the need for NHS-funded care; and the range, type, location and level of services to be arranged and funded by the NHS to meet continuing healthcare needs in each area. These policies had to be agreed with social services and be operable from 1 April 1996. They define the boundaries of NHS responsibilities at the local level and the limits to the care that it will provide.

17. The DoH's guidance explicitly required purchasers to arrange a full range of services including continuing inpatient care, community health services and rehabilitation. The guidance re-affirmed continuing healthcare as a critical third component of the NHS alongside primary and secondary care; and it defined the main services that make up continuing healthcare [**EXHIBIT 9, overleaf**].

18. However, few additional resources were made available for implementation, 'Challenge Fund' monies being the major source (£20 million in 1996/97, £25 million – with requirements that health authorities match the funding – in 1997/98) (Ref. 13). Otherwise resources must be found from within existing budgets. Failure to do so could place a burden on others – particularly older people themselves and their carers as well as social services – that could become unsustainable. The first legacy of the 1980s that needs managing is the change to the cut-off point at which the NHS stops providing care.

EXHIBIT 9

Continuing healthcare services

Continuing healthcare is a critical third component of the NHS.

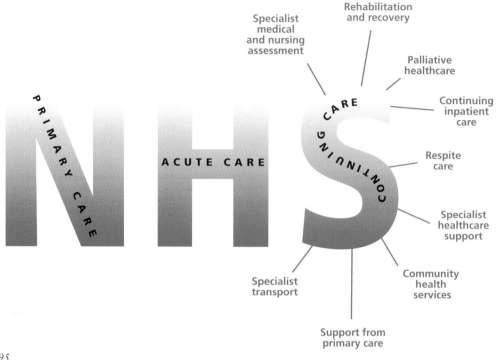

Source: HSG (95) 8, DoH, 1995

The growth in the provision of care by the private and voluntary sectors

19. The second legacy of the 1980s has been a significant shift from the public to the independent sector in the provision of care [**EXHIBIT 10**]. In the whole of the UK in 1983, NHS beds and local authority residential care beds accounted for 59 per cent of total provision: by 1996 this had fallen to only 20 per cent of total provision. In part this decrease was due to a growth in places overall from 312,500 in 1983 to 550,000 in 1996; in part it was due to an actual reduction in public sector provision.

EXHIBIT 10

The shift from public to independent sector provision of care

A legacy of the 1980s has been a significant shift from the public to the independent sector in the provision of care.

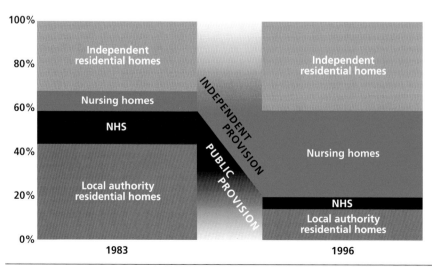

Source: Care of Elderly People Market Survey, Laing and Buisson, 1997

20. This shift gives users and their carers a wider range of choice, opens up the care sector to new ideas and fresh capital, and exerts pressure on service providers to contain costs and improve quality. But it must be properly co-ordinated. Some social services departments have been slow to come to terms with a mixed economy of care, partly because the skills needed to relate to the independent sector are very different from those traditionally available in social services departments. To ensure that they made increasing use of the independent sector, part of the special transitional grant was restricted for provision of services in the independent sector.[1] The independent sector is a major player and it must be integrated effectively with the care system.

The role of social services

21. As a result of the NHS and Community Care Act 1990, social services are now caught between the NHS and independent sectors and must address these two major legacies. On the one hand they face a steady stream of referrals coming to them from the NHS. As these represent a major component of the demand for their services, NHS decisions about what it will or will not do impact directly on the workload of social services. On the other hand, social services must also work with the independent sector to secure the supply of services and this role requires new skills and procedures.

22. This arrangement was intended to clarify a smooth pathway for people to go back to their own homes where possible from hospital, or on to residential or nursing homes where not [EXHIBIT 11]. Placed centrally between the NHS and independent sectors, social services encounter difficulties at both these interfaces. While recognising that not all those receiving community care experience difficulties related to these interfaces, this report focuses on them as the key pressure points within the system.

---

[1]   Eighty-five per cent of STG in the first four years.

EXHIBIT 11

The route from hospital into community care

Social services are placed centrally between the NHS and independent sectors.

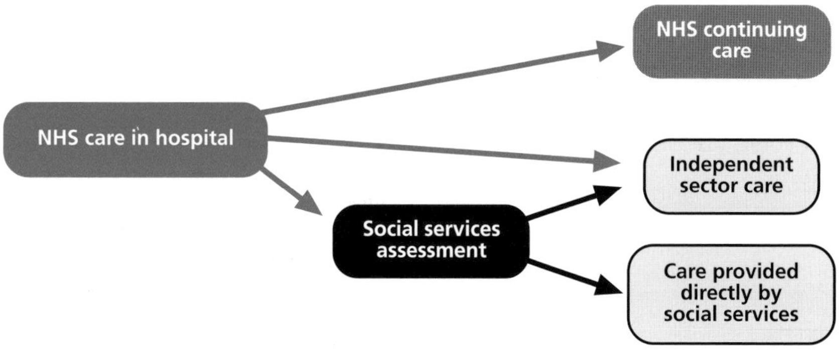

Source: Audit Commission

23. The impact of any inadequacies in arrangements for providing continuing care is felt most immediately by older people themselves and their families. Chapter 2 looks at arrangements from the older person's point of view, following the trail from initial referral while in hospital through to assessment, the planning of care and the setting up of services. It concentrates on the 'baton changes' between health, social services and the independent sector, and highlights the points at which the baton is most frequently dropped and the steps that some authorities are taking to avoid these difficulties.

24. But simply streamlining operational procedures is not enough. Health and social services must establish a framework within which these procedures can operate, and Chapter 3 looks at the changes required in the way that services are planned. Chapter 4 goes on to consider the issues that need to be addressed nationally if the opportunities open to both health and social services authorities are to be fully realised and care for older people is to be delivered in a coherent and effective way.

2

Assessing and Arranging Care

Older people often experience care services that are poorly co-ordinated. All too often health and social services fail to agree their respective responsibilities, resulting in confusion and sometimes delays to discharge from hospital. Access to information about services is patchy and staff often do not have the flexibility to tailor services effectively. Where initiatives have been taken, the services and choices available to older people have been improved significantly.

25. This chapter focuses on the paths that older people typically follow from hospital back into the community. The process of arranging their discharge from hospital involves a number of basic steps [EXHIBIT 12].

26. After admission to hospital, those likely to require continuing care are referred for assessment. Ideally, the referral should be made as soon as possible after admission to allow plenty of time to plan for discharge and beyond. If all relevant parties agree that care is going to be needed, a care plan is drawn up that sets out the services required. The assessment and care planning processes should involve both health and social services staff working together; for those who do not require a continuing health involvement, services are usually arranged by social services staff, often using independent providers. There are two distinct stages: assessment and planning for discharge, and arranging services.

EXHIBIT 12

The process of planning and arranging community care for those in hospital

The process of arranging discharge from hospital involves a number of basic steps by different agencies.

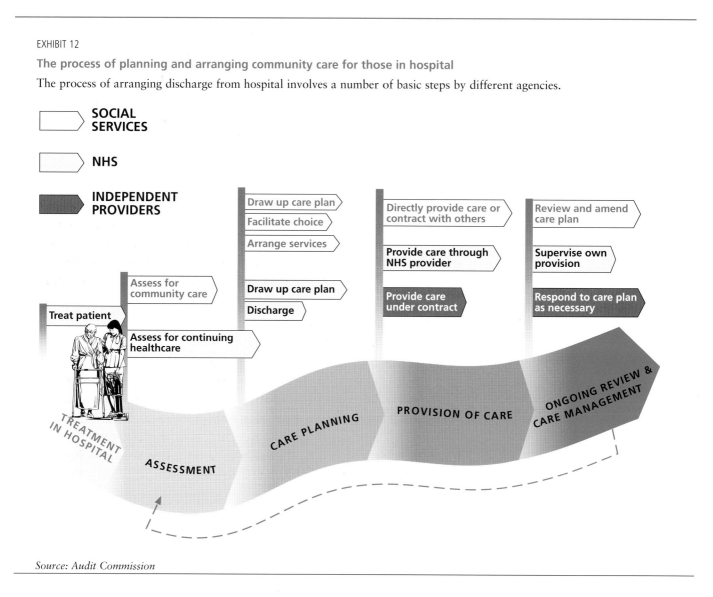

Source: Audit Commission

Assessment and planning for discharge

27. Assessment involves working with older people to identify whether they require care in the medium to long term – known as 'continuing' care. Although the process varies from one locality to another, social services care managers play a key role in co-ordinating this process with hospital staff.

28. In many parts of the country, continuing care arrangements are dogged by disputes that result in 'blocked beds' – hospital beds that are occupied by people who are considered by hospital staff not to need hospital care but for one reason or another are unable to leave. Some of these disputes arise because the overall pattern of services has not been properly planned in an integrated way (see the next chapter). But others are caused by poor operational procedures. Problems often occur in three key parts of the discharge process:

- failure to agree responsibilities between hospital and social services staff;

- failure to set reasonable time standards; and

- inconsistent assessment procedures leading to poor quality assessments.

Older people are on the receiving end of such problems and this can damage their self-esteem, especially where they are already having difficulty coming to terms with their new circumstances.

Agreeing responsibilities

29. Difficulties occur where it is not clear who should be doing what. In order to work effectively together, health and social service staff need to agree who is responsible for different stages of the discharge process and monitor whether these responsibilities are being met. At this point the definitions of what each agency will or will not do can become the focus for the dispute.

30. In one hospital which experienced delays, staff decided to work with their social services colleagues to analyse the problem. Prior to agreeing definitions they had thought that social services were responsible for the majority of delays, but once definitions were in place they found that many of the delays were caused by problems within the hospital, which they could address directly themselves [EXHIBIT 13, overleaf]. Some delays were caused by inactivity in other parts of the health service, and yet others by a lack of agreement about what should happen next – often in situations where relatives refused to accept that a discharge from hospital was appropriate.

EXHIBIT 13

Discharge delays

Prior to agreeing definitions, the staff of one hospital had thought social services responsible for the majority of delays, but with definitions in place they found that many of the delays were caused by problems within the hospital, which they could address directly themselves.

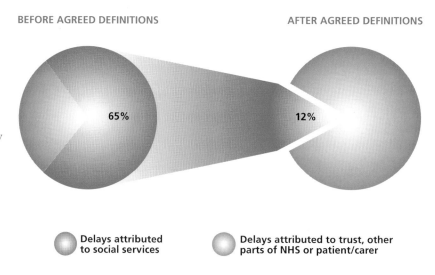

BEFORE AGREED DEFINITIONS

AFTER AGREED DEFINITIONS

65%

12%

● **Delays attributed to social services**

○ **Delays attributed to trust, other parts of NHS or patient/carer**

Source: Audit Commission study site

31. Clear definitions of responsibility should be supported by robust and regular monitoring to identify the causes of delay. Often the trust can take action itself to ease difficulties; for example, simplify the process of transferring people to other facilities by introducing a clear set of procedures. Monitoring may also indicate where action is needed by the health authority; for example, by providing additional facilities that help to get people ready to leave hospital. And, finally, monitoring should indicate where social services are failing to meet their responsibilities.

32. Health and social services authorities also need to ensure that procedures are carried out to a high standard. In busy hospitals and in the community, staff need periodic reminders of the importance and relevance of particular processes and procedures, and regular audits can make the process clearer to all involved. In one authority, an acute trust and community trust have developed an operational policy together for admission, assessment, transfer and discharge of patients from hospital, supported by a comprehensive programme of audit and monitoring [CASE STUDY 1].

RECOMMENDATION

Health trusts and social services staff should agree their respective responsibilities for different stages of the discharge process. They should undertake a joint audit of all alleged discharge delays and identify the agency responsible.

CASE STUDY 1

Quality audits of hospital discharge

The Royal Cornwall Hospitals Acute Trust and the Cornwall Community Healthcare Trust have jointly developed an operational policy for admission, assessment, transfer and discharge of patients from hospital. A discharge team is in place to improve discharge planning, bridging the communication gap between secondary and primary healthcare and social services. It comprises:

- a discharge nurse trainer;
- a discharge liaison nurses (link with primary healthcare);
- a discharge hospital co-ordinators (link with social services); and
- a discharge audit nurse.

The acute trust's nursing documentation has a discharge assessment tool which is completed on admission and which facilitates early identification of need for referral to social services.

The policy sets out the expected standards to be achieved for discharge planning. The discharge audit nurse follows up all aspects of the policy – 'to enable staff to learn and improve as a result'. A whole range of audits has been completed; for example:

- an audit of referrals from hospital wards to check that discharge checklists were properly completed for patients;

- an audit to examine the effectiveness of patient transfer from the district general hospital to community or elderly care hospitals; and
- an audit of hospital re-admissions.

In addition, regular monitoring is carried out of:

- standards agreed with social services;
- reasons for delayed discharge; and
- hospital discharge co-ordinators' workload.

Setting time standards

33. Agencies need to check the promptness with which actions are taken. People should not be left languishing in hospital for long periods unnecessarily. Recovery (and certainly morale) can be improved by prompt action. Social services, the hospital and the health authority should agree time standards for assessment, care planning and discharge procedures. These standards need to allow for the complexity of the task: it takes time to assess, allow choice and arrange care. If someone has been assessed as medically fit, but is still being assessed for discharge within jointly agreed standards, the bed is not 'blocked', and its occupant should not be made to feel a nuisance in the meantime.

34. The Commission found that time standards are often not specified and vary widely where they are [**EXHIBIT 14**]. Only two out of the eleven social services departments had agreed times for all processes. Six had

EXHIBIT 14

Assessment time standards found in fieldwork authorities

Most authorities have not specified time standards for key stages of the process and in those that have, a wide range of standards is used.

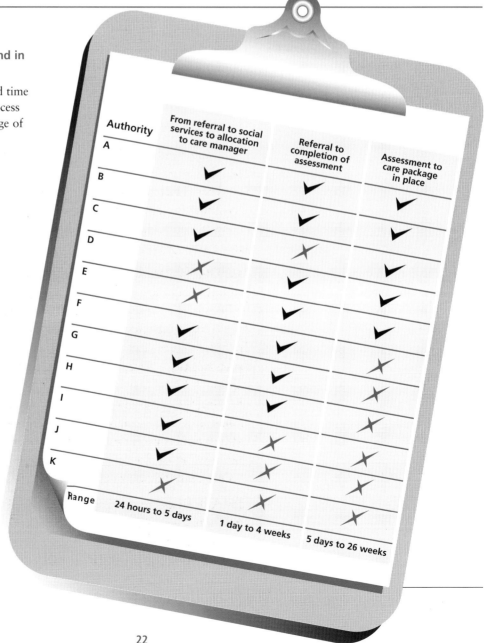

Authority	From referral to social services to allocation to care manager	Referral to completion of assessment	Assessment to care package in place
A			
B	✔	✔	
C	✔	✔	✔
D	✔	✔	✔
E	✗	✗	✔
F	✗	✔	✔
G	✔	✔	✔
H	✔	✔	✗
I	✔	✔	✗
J	✔	✔	✗
K	✔	✗	✗
Range	24 hours to 5 days	1 day to 4 weeks	5 days to 26 weeks

Source: Audit Commission fieldwork

22

Evidence shows that more ambitious assessment standards can be achieved...

apparently not agreed a time to put a care package in place after completing the assessment. And of those departments which had, one had a standard of 26 weeks, leaving people with the prospect of waiting up to six months for their care. The absence of agreed time standards is a recipe for confusion and recrimination.

35. Evidence shows that more ambitious assessment standards can be achieved, even across large, dispersed authorities. For example, one social services department provides 93 per cent of care packages within five days of receipt of the referral for services. This promptness is achieved despite having to arrange discharges from 26 different hospitals across a large area. Some of the achievement can be explained by clear, delegated responsibility within the department and good co-ordination with acute and community health services.

RECOMMENDATION

Social services staff should agree time standards with health trusts (and with health authorities as necessary) for key milestones in the implementation of a care package. Trusts should make an officer responsible for monitoring discharge delays on a regular basis, identifying who is responsible and checking time standards, and reporting to the trust's chief executive and director of social services.

Improving assessment procedures

36. Assessment must be accurate, since in many cases it affects where people spend the rest of their lives. It is the process that determines whether someone can be cared for at home or whether a period of rehabilitation and recovery is necessary; whether continuing care in a hospital is required or whether a nursing home or a residential home is more appropriate.

37. One danger of poor assessment is that people may receive more services than they need, such as a hospital bed rather than care at home, or a nursing home place rather than a place in a residential home. This phenomenon is often referred to as 'upward substitution'. A recent survey of older people in nursing homes found that many had been wrongly assessed (Ref. 14). Only 11 per cent definitely needed nursing home care although 54 per cent probably needed it; but one in three were considered fit enough to return home or to receive care in, at most, a residential home. Documentation was poor: there was no medical information for 40 per cent of cases, no social information for 70 per cent, no nursing information for 35 per cent, no occupational therapy information for 93 per cent and no physiotherapy information for 90 per cent.

38. A fieldwork authority noted: 'Some discharges to nursing and residential homes are premature. Audit has shown that at least 5 per cent could return to their own homes with further rehabilitation and recovery, and this is considered to be an underestimate.' Older people thus risk

...professionals must... provide a rounded picture of all health and social needs...

becoming more dependent through too much care, and resources are denied to others who might benefit from them. Those with lesser (but still substantial) needs get nothing at all as resources are used up by those with greater needs. The difficulties are compounded where care options are inflexible or limited, or where there are poor rehabilitation services, so that expensive options are the only ones available.

39. A particular problem is poor co-ordination between professionals. Although care managers take the lead role in assessment, other professionals must be involved in more complex cases to provide a rounded picture of all health and social needs: for example, input from health professionals is needed to identify health needs. But this co-ordination is difficult. One member of staff referred to the twin dangers of either no assessment or 'serial assessment' by a myriad of professionals. One health authority found a high level of inappropriate assessment, poor co-ordination and poor documentation, and introduced major changes as a result [CASE STUDY 2]. Another found that assessment and discharge arrangements were poorly carried out for older people in specialties other than geriatrics [CASE STUDY 3].

EXHIBIT 15

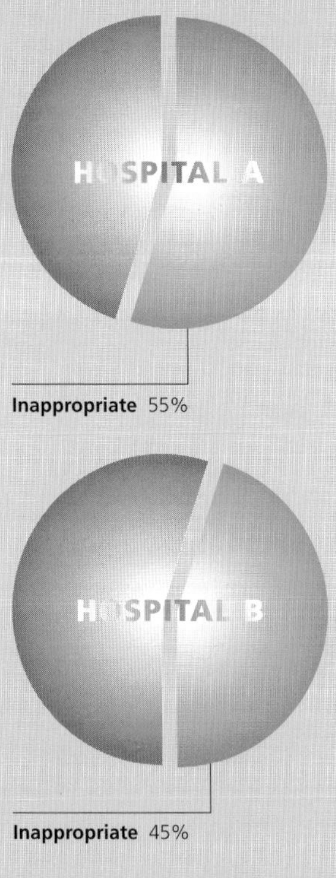

HOSPITAL A

Inappropriate 55%

HOSPITAL B

Inappropriate 45%

CASE STUDY 2

Audit of appropriateness of assessment

One health authority, worried about delayed discharges and inconsistencies, set up a small-scale audit of hospital discharges of older people from two main sites. The audit found that at Hospital A, 55 per cent of assessments were inappropriate, and 45 per cent were inappropriate at Hospital B [EXHIBIT 15].

The audit revealed that:

- there was poor co-ordination of multidisciplinary assessment and a lack of clarity about how to trigger it;

- the district nurse liaison officer had a very limited role in assessing cases, even though some patients had previously been known to the district nursing service and were being considered for home care;

- there was uncertainty about how health and social services resources could be accessed;

- there was no re-assessment to reflect the fact that patients' conditions or home circumstances could change considerably over time; and

- documentation was poor – it was impossible to tell from casenotes who attended ward meetings/case conferences or what had been decided.

As a result of these findings, a further project on the care management of older people was established with the aim of standardising the assessment procedure, identifying the triggers for inter-agency assessment and promoting ongoing training for all operational staff.

CASE STUDY 3

Bromley Health Authority Intensive Continuing Care Resource Project

The six-month Intensive Continuing Care Resource Unit Project aimed to identify hospitalised patients with continuing healthcare needs and develop a strategy to ensure easy access to such care, where appropriate. The project was also designed to test draft continuing care eligibility criteria prior to implementation in April 1996. Discharge planning for patients with a complex disability was to continue to be undertaken by existing multidisciplinary ward teams. Referral to the project was restricted to patients where continuing healthcare needs were unclear or where there was a lack of community provision for known healthcare needs at discharge. The project:

- established a team to assess continuing healthcare need and provide specialist skills throughout a hospital supported by six inpatient beds (maximum length of stay two weeks); and

- could 'spot purchase' healthcare provision for a maximum of seven days to bridge the gap between discharge and availability of community services.

Evaluation of the project found that application of defined eligibility criteria in mainstream practice was problematic. In particular, 'assessment of continuing care need is based on an unstandardised and often erroneous application of the core process of assessments by professionals not trained in the management of complex disability' (Ref. 15). Clear and explicit guidance was given to staff on the aims and objectives of the project, mode of referral, details of the target patient group and services offered.

Even so, only 38 per cent of patients referred to the specialist unit were eligible for intervention. The evaluation report concluded that 'continuing care needs were poorly recognised by treating physicians and the multidisciplinary team in specialties other than geriatrics'.

The service was revised, resulting in a new contract with the acute trusts. This includes spot purchasing, multidisciplinary co-ordination within the hospital across specialties and a designated (funded) consultant appointed to co-ordinate continuing care clinical awareness.

40. Eight of the eleven social services departments visited had no checks on the quality of assessments prior to admission to nursing or residential homes. However, three had multidisciplinary panels that considered completed assessments to ensure that:

- responsibilities were discussed and funding agreed by the appropriate authority;

- all health and/or social care needs had been examined; and

- all alternatives to residential or nursing home care had been explored to ensure that any residential or nursing home placements were absolutely necessary.

EXHIBIT 16

Authorities with multidisciplinary assessment panels

Where multidisciplinary assessment panels are in place, the number of older people in nursing or residential homes is well below the average.

Residential care receivers per 1,000 75+ population in 1996

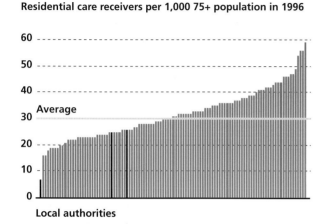

Local authorities

Nursing care receivers per 1,000 75+ population in 1996

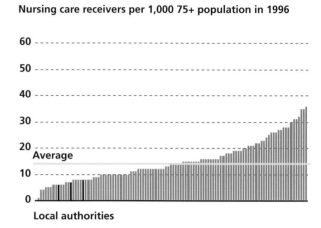

Local authorities

▌ Multidisciplinary assessment panels in place

Source: Audit Commission fieldwork; Key Indicators, 0A35, 0A45, DoH, May 1997

41. Such panels are not a panacea. They can become bureaucratic – meeting irregularly and slowing down decisions, placements and discharges from hospital. But where they are flexible, well managed, multidisciplinary and multi-agency, they can help to ensure that scarce resources are used for those older people who really need them. Panels that function well can also enable professionals to share skills; it may be possible to restrict their use once these skills have been learned. In all three authorities with such panels, the numbers receiving local authority-funded residential and nursing home care (standardised for age) were well below average [EXHIBIT 16].

42. Better links with geriatric medicine can help to identify treatable illnesses and opportunities for rehabilitation. In Australia the development of geriatric assessment teams (GATs) has succeeded in achieving a degree of 'downward substitution' with decreased use of nursing home beds (Ref. 16). Assessment by an approved assessment team is mandatory before an admission can be made to a nursing home; and assessment guidelines provide a framework for the team.

RECOMMENDATION

Health trusts and social services staff should review assessment arrangements, clarifying responsibilities for different members of staff, standardising procedures and documentation and monitoring the completion of documentation. They should consider introducing panels to monitor proposed placements in residential and nursing homes and establishing links with geriatric medicine.

43. But effective partnerships between health and social services to work out what is needed are only part of the solution. People must then be provided with appropriate services and this requires effective care planning and working with service providers. This process is described in the next section.

Arranging services

44. Care services should be co-ordinated to suit each person. Services that aim to meet health needs can be arranged and provided by the NHS, in which case they are defined as 'continuing *health*care' and are also funded by the NHS. Social care is organised by local authority social services departments. It is usually means-tested and often requires a contribution from the individual. Authorities are increasingly establishing care managers to assess needs and then design packages of care within a framework set up by the centre [**EXHIBIT 17, overleaf**]. Older people and their carers are at the heart of the framework, since care managers need to work closely with them if they are to devise care packages that suit them. But all four main groups need to interact: those planning services at the centre[1] need to understand what users want and how this might change in future; and providers need to be responsive to those who receive services. Communication between all those helping to arrange and provide services needs to be effective. This section focuses on the care manager's role with older people and their carers, drawing up care plans and arranging services. The role of the centre in setting up the overall framework is discussed in the next chapter.

45. The framework set out above does not always lead to effective tailoring of care packages, principally for the following reasons:

- older people and their carers do not appear to have as much influence over their care as they could;

- care managers have limited choice to offer older people; and

- subsequent reviews of services, to ensure they continue to be appropriate, often receive a low priority.

---

[1]   Refers to social services planning, commissioning, finance and senior management staff.

EXHIBIT 17

Framework for commissioning community care services

All four key groups involved in the commissioning of services must communicate effectively to shape services that meet people's needs.

Source: Audit Commission

Involving older people

46. Older people and their carers need to understand the care management process and the options available to them. This means keeping them informed. Research conducted by the Joint Reviews of Social Services[1] showed that only 23 per cent of users and carers have had any information on the services available from social services before coming into contact with them. Thirty-eight per cent do not receive anything in writing subsequently about the help or services that social services are going to provide; 57 per cent claim that they have not been told how to make a complaint, and only half of those who actually do complain feel that their complaint was dealt with satisfactorily. The team also found that carers' assessments, which aim to accommodate the specific needs of the carer (which may be different from those of the service user), were not taking place routinely (Ref. 17). Other research has shown that users of home care services do not always find that services are as responsive as they would like [BOX A].

BOX A

Extracts from older people's views of home care services

Services do not always take place as planned, or in a way that suits older people.

'Service users mentioned the problems they had when a home carer did not arrive when they were expected. Typically, when such situations arose, no one would contact the service users to advise them what was happening, why there was a delay, whether care staff would be along later, or if someone else was visiting instead...'

'Several service users remarked ... that they would be happy to go without particular help on some occasions if it meant that they could substitute another form of support within the time allocated...'

'One elderly woman...described how her carer would arrive to help her to bed around 8pm, and not return until after 9.30am the following morning...'

'A recurrent issue among a minority of service users was the desire for help which did not seem to be within the remit of a standard home care service. Some users told us... help in getting outside and going for a walk in the fresh air would make a significant contribution to their quality of life...'

Source: Developing and Evaluating User-centred Outcomes for Domiciliary Care Services, Nuffield and UKHCA, 1997

---

1   Results of 1,113 users and carers surveyed in the review of the first ten authorities.

Older people and their carers need information if they are to make effective choices.

47. Involving users and carers not only leads to greater satisfaction, but it can also lead to greater cost-effectiveness. Evidence from the Independent Living Fund shows that when users of social services are fully involved by being given their own funds, they often develop very cost-effective packages (Ref. 18). This option is not available to older people, and even if it were it is not clear that all service users would want to manage their own care. Care managers should therefore ensure that older people and their carers are fully involved in deciding the type of care to be provided.

48. Older people and their carers need information if they are to make effective choices. This applies equally to those whom the authority is unable to support financially. All authorities visited by the Commission produced directories of care homes listing names and addresses of proprietors, but few provide information on what a home is like. The directories also focus on registered homes and ignore other options such as sheltered housing. Information on non-residential services is often unavailable. At what is likely to be a distressing time in people's lives, care managers should be in a position to provide guidance. Social services should therefore build up directories of services to help people to make informed choices between the options available.

49. Vulnerable people, such as those in care homes, may also benefit from support from independent advocates to enable them to voice concerns that they might not wish to raise with their care manager [CASE STUDY 4].

RECOMMENDATION

Social services departments should ensure that older people and their carers are fully informed and involved in the care management process. They should provide information about the process, about the full range of choices available (in the form of directories), about ways of complaining and of changing services where necessary. They should consider the use of advocacy for older people.

The idea was to link the advocacy to the review of residents' care...

CASE STUDY 4

Developing a focused advocacy service in Tameside Social Services Department

In 1995 the Citizen's Advice Bureau in Tameside approached the Social Services Department with a proposal to develop an advocacy scheme for older or disabled people who were receiving residential or nursing home care funded by the Department. The idea was to link the advocacy to the review of residents' care undertaken within the home. The Department funded a pilot scheme at a cost of approximately £50,000 per year. The objectives of the scheme were:

- to review independently the needs of users as set out in their care plan and to assess whether they continue to be met by the service;
- to judge whether the service is continuing to meet needs; and
- to help the person gain access to any further or different services if necessary.

The scheme was implemented after consultation with people who run residential homes and their trade associations. Initial difficulties occurred in ensuring that providers distinguished between advocacy and contract monitoring. These problems have diminished as the scheme has developed.

An independent evaluation showed that between January and September 1996 the project managed to make contact with 733 clients in residential and nursing homes, had arranged 196 pre-review meetings with clients and attended 157 reviews. In 77 per cent of the reviews attended issues were raised on behalf of the service user by the advocate. These resulted in such diverse outcomes as:

- investigating and assuring a homeowner that a relative was not defrauding a resident of their money;
- ensuring that a resident had access to continence pads which he had been too embarrassed to ask for, although they were in the care plan;
- arranging for a resident to have a single room when she had not complained for fear of upsetting staff at the home; and
- the relocation of a nursing home resident who had made some recovery and wanted to move to a residential home (both improving the resident's satisfaction and saving money).

The scheme has recently been extended to provide advocacy during the initial placement and at the first review after six weeks. This development is acting as an important check:

- to ensure that the issue of user choice is addressed properly;
- to examine whether care plan objectives are still applicable given the probable change in circumstances;
- to offer an independent perspective as to whether the placement is appropriate; and
- to help to deal with any financial problems.

...care managers need to be able to put together the best care packages.

Increasing the options available to care managers

50. Even where assessment processes are of a high standard and service users are able to exert influence, care managers themselves need to be able to put together the best care packages. But often their hands are tied by the framework set by the centre. The most significant constraints are:

- restrictions on the choice of service provider, combined with a lack of ability to influence what is provided;

- a general lack of skills and confidence in some care management tasks; and

- lack of control over budgets for service provision.

51. In many authorities, care managers are limited in their choice of provider [**EXHIBIT 18**]. Two-thirds of authorities operated 'in-house first' policies with their direct home care provider, even though these providers were often inflexible, restricting the hours in which they were prepared to supply services and the tasks they were prepared to perform. Independent home care providers tended to be used only to supplement the local authority service, often providing services at times when the local authority service was not operating or meeting the needs of 'difficult' cases. As a result, it was not uncommon for older people to have fragmented packages from more than one source; independent providers for their part were left with haphazard demand for their services.

EXHIBIT 18

Restrictions placed on care managers by local authority providers

The need to use services set up in-house has led to restrictions on choice.

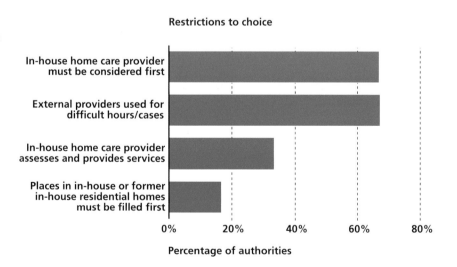

Restrictions to choice

Source: Audit Commission fieldwork

52. Where older people were placed in residential care, two authorities were directing those who did not express a preference to their own residential homes, or to those of a former local authority provider. While authorities' desire to make full use of their own pre-paid provision is understandable, there appears to be no check that these are the most appropriate and cost-effective available. Some authorities argue that because independent sector providers pay low wages, they use their in-house provider to offer reasonably waged employment as part of an anti-poverty strategy. However, the cost-effectiveness of care should be the primary consideration and, if necessary, indicative pay rates can also be built into external contracts.

53. Furthermore, care managers' ability to exert any influence over the nature of local authority services is often limited. If they are to have any influence, they need some basic information on the costs and quality of provision and some leverage over providers. Most authorities have made progress in calculating unit costs, although care managers are not always made aware of them. But only one-third of authorities had service level agreements with their own providers, setting out what care managers could expect [EXHIBIT 19]. Local authority providers themselves expressed some dissatisfaction that, in the absence of a such agreements, their ability to offer a more attractive and responsive service is currently constrained. Some authorities have gone further with the introduction of trading arrangements and full choice between providers [CASE STUDY 5, OVERLEAF].

EXHIBIT 19

Steps in strengthening commissioning from in-house home care providers

Accurate unit costs and service agreements are the first steps to ensuring value for money.

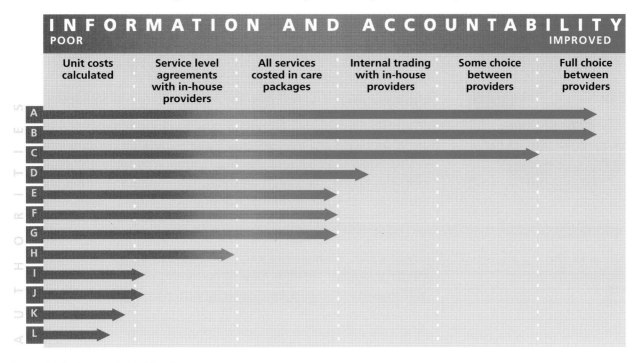

Source: Audit Commission fieldwork

54. Cultural barriers to local commissioning remain strong. Many care managers do not see cost awareness as part of their job. Both national training and training within authorities need to help to develop purchasing skills in care management. But while training is necessary it is not in itself sufficient: other approaches should also be used to increase confidence. Finance staff working alongside care management teams in two fieldwork authorities enabled them to manage their budgets with greater expertise and confidence.

55. Care managers express concern that tightening budgets are limiting their ability to try more innovative care packages. Pressures on budgets have led most authorities to specify the maximum amount per week that they are prepared to allow for care packages, particularly for older people. All but one of the twelve authorities visited operated such limits, with the gross or net cost of residential care usually being used to define the limit for a home care package. Unfortunately, this practice discourages care managers, for example, from putting together intensive, short-term care packages (for people leaving hospital) to prevent or delay a residential care admission in the longer term. Greater flexibility might improve both outcomes and unit costs.

56. They were also worried about potential legal problems and risk; for example, using a non-accredited provider or putting together a non-standard package, such as arranging for local restaurants to deliver meals. Some staff voiced concerns over a tendency to place users in residential and nursing homes, where they receive round-the-clock supervision, to limit any risk to the authority. Almost two-thirds of gross expenditure on services for older people in England is on services in residential settings **[EXHIBIT 20]**.

57. But even where a home care package is provided, it is often in a standard form: the most recent statistics show that 40 per cent of visits are for less than two hours and 31 per cent of users are getting just one visit a week (Ref.19). While recognising that these packages might be enabling a carer to take a break from his or her duties, authorities should check that the type of care that they offer is appropriate for each individual.

58. Many of the problems associated with commissioning from in-house providers were caused by the funding structures: in-house budgets were typically separate and treated differently from budgets for independent sector providers. In one-third of fieldwork authorities, budgets were still held by the centre (at service manager level); in one-half they were held at team manager level. In only one-sixth of authorities were they held by frontline care managers and where this was the case, it was only for limited purposes – typically for spot purchasing of home care from the independent sector. As a result some services were apparently 'free' to care managers since they were not charged to their budgets. This could distort the pattern of services, since these services were naturally offered first to older people, and so appeared to be more popular.

EXHIBIT 20

Gross local authority spend on services for the 75 plus age group (England, 1995/96)

Sixty-four per cent of spend on social services in England was on care in residential settings.

Nursing home care 18%

Residential care 46%

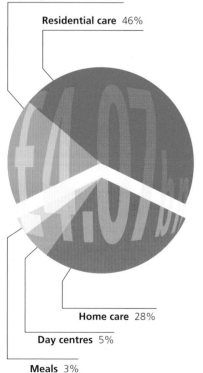

Home care 28%

Day centres 5%

Meals 3%

Source: DoH, Key Indicators Graphical System

59. Devolving budgets to care managers (or teams of care managers) enables decisions about where resources are to be spent to be taken by those who are planning care with older people [CASE STUDY 5]. But, crucially, devolved budgeting requires sound financial systems if financial difficulties and administrative paperchases are to be avoided.

RECOMMENDATION

Social services should ensure that care managers have greater influence over services by reducing restrictions on choice, introducing service level agreements with in-house providers and delegating budgets at least to teams, (providing that financial controls and advice are in place). Authorities should ensure that the unit costs of in-house services are calculated and that care managers are aware of them.

CASE STUDY 5

Setting up an internal trading system

At the start of the implementation of the community care reforms, Kensington and Chelsea Social Services Department recognised that if it was to be able to commission efficiently and effectively and to meet needs then the costs of in-house, as well as externally purchased, services needed to be clear and accountable to purchasers. The authority decided to establish an internal trading mechanism for the in-house home care service.

Detailed analysis was undertaken to determine appropriate allocations of management and support service costs, both from within the Social Services Department and other council services. After pilot work during 1993/94, the trading account became operational in 1994/95.

The system initially had teething problems. Contact hours data were calculated from a sample analysis of 'productive time' (that is, excluding training, travel and other non-contact time). This analysis proved problematic, requiring a mid-year price adjustment in 1994/95 to balance the trading account. To improve the accuracy of the data, productive time is now estimated more realistically and in more detail. Contact hours are based on data compiled directly from timesheets and are input into the home care IT system.

The internal trading arrangement has developed further into a type of cost and volume contract. The provider is guaranteed approximately 80 per cent of its capacity with 20 per cent being available for purchase by care management teams on a spot basis. Pressure is building to allow a greater proportion of hours to be purchased on a spot-contract basis.

Despite the difficulties, officers remain positive about the benefits of operating an internal trading process. Key advantages have focused on:

- the pressure exerted through the system to improve productivity, principally by reducing non-contact time;

- the drive to develop more robust management information with which to manage the service; and

- the visibility given to management and support costs.

Improved management information has, in turn, helped to provide data on which to make more informed judgements about wider commissioning issues, such as what services should be contracted from the independent sector and what the best future use of the in-house home care service should be.

Although operating such a system has costs in terms of staff time, officers noted that these had diminished as the system had developed, and estimated that they now accounted for less than one full-time officer post.

The internal trading system is now supported by a service level agreement with the purchaser section. This has helped to clarify what services are to be delivered and the service standards expected, giving care management a greater say in shaping the service to meet their needs.

Care needs for most individuals fluctuate and so packages also need to be flexible.

Reviewing and monitoring

60. Care managers must monitor and review care packages to check that they continue to be appropriate and achieve their aims. They also need to check that users are happy with the quality of the services that they are receiving. Care needs for most individuals fluctuate and so packages also need to be flexible. Packages which initially meet a need (after discharge from hospital, for example) can be reduced as the user regains confidence, saving unnecessary expenditure [CASE STUDY 6].

61. However, in most authorities visited care managers complained that their heavy assessment workloads made it difficult for them to find time for reviews. Ongoing care management is often limited to those in residential settings and packages of home care are less likely to be reviewed. Joint Reviews have found wide variations between authorities in the proportion of service users who claim to have been asked 'how things are working out' with their care package – from 43 per cent to 77 per cent of respondents (Ref. 17).

62. Some fieldwork authorities have introduced central teams to review and monitor care packages, but these tend to be small (typically one to three full-time equivalent staff) and cannot make much impact on the thousands of home care users (let alone on users of other services). Not one authority was able to cite the amount of time that care managers actually spend reviewing; more work needs to be done on understanding care managers' workloads. If reviews by care managers are not possible for all service users, authorities could make alternative arrangements – such as the advocacy scheme in Case Study 4, or the review of all service users described in Case Study 6 – to ensure that all users have access to advice and information throughout the care process, and not just at the beginning or in the event of a crisis.

CASE STUDY 6

Ensuring that care packages are cost-effective

In 1995, following the introduction of eligibility criteria, Buckinghamshire Social Services Department instigated a review of home care packages provided by the local authority provider and external providers.

To date they have assessed 3,474 clients. Reassessments of needs enabled them to identify packages that were not meeting users' needs: 14 per cent were no longer deemed a priority and so their packages ceased; 42 per cent of users had their packages reduced, but this was compensated by 44 per cent where more care was needed. In effect, the exercise has enabled the Department to target resources more effectively.

RECOMMENDATION

Social services should undertake a systematic review of packages of home care where this has not been done recently. Social services should ensure that procedures are in place to review services regularly to check that care plans are being achieved and that resources are continuing to be used to best effect. If necessary, they should review the workload of care managers.

Conclusion

63. More attention is needed at the local level to the way that care is organised and managed to improve the quality and flexibility of the process. But the impact of better operational practices will be limited by the services available. Local staff cannot commission services that do not already exist. The centre has to play its part by providing incentives for providers to realign their services through contracting and market management. This is the subject of the next chapter.

RECOMMENDATIONS

2   Assessing and Arranging Care

Managing discharge

1   Health trusts and social services staff should agree their respective responsibilities for different stages of the discharge process.

2   They should undertake a joint audit of all alleged discharge delays and identify who is responsible.

3   Social services staff should agree time standards with health trusts (and with health authorities as necessary) for the key stages in the implementation of a care package.

4   Trusts should make an officer responsible for monitoring discharge delays on a regular basis, identifying who is responsible and checking time standards, and reporting to the trust's chief executive and director of social services.

5   Health trusts and social services staff should review assessment arrangements, clarifying responsibilities for different members of staff, standardising procedures and documentation and monitoring the completion of documentation. They should consider introducing panels to monitor proposed placements in residential and nursing homes.

Strengthening care management

6   Social services should ensure that older people and their carers are fully informed and involved in the care management process by providing information about the process, about the full range of choices available (in the form of directories), ways of complaining and ways of changing services where necessary. They should consider the use of advocacy for older people.

7   Social services should ensure that care managers have greater influence over services by reducing restrictions on choice, introducing service level agreements with in-house providers and delegating budgets at least to teams, providing financial controls and advice are in place. Authorities should ensure that unit costs of in-house services are calculated and available to care managers.

8   Social services should undertake a systematic review of packages of home care where this has not been done recently.

9   Social services should ensure that procedures are in place to review services regularly to check that care plans are being achieved and that resources are continuing to be used to best effect. If necessary, they should review the workload of care managers.

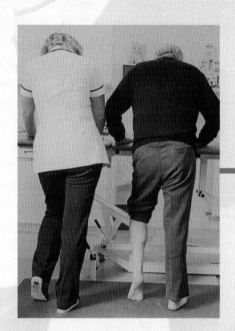

3

Rebalancing Services

The NHS and social services appear to be locked in a vicious circle with heavy emphasis placed on the use of acute beds and care in residential settings, making it difficult to free up the resources for alternative services that might begin to ease the pressure. Both agencies need to work together to devise new initiatives to rebalance services. Health services need to explore alternatives to hospital. Social services need to develop better relationships with independent providers to secure a wider range of quality services.

64. Authorities must plan and work with providers to rebalance services where the current pattern of provision does not reflect users' and practitioners' preferences. For health authorities, this means working with trusts; for social services, this means working increasingly with the independent sector. For both agencies, it means working closer together, generating comparable information and planning the development of services jointly [EXHIBIT 21]. But both have been under increasing pressure which has made working together more difficult and the achievement of an effective balance of services less likely.

Pressures on the NHS

65. Health authorities and trusts are under pressure from:

- a rise in the rate of emergency admissions;

- pressures to reduce lengths of stay; and

- insufficient 'intermediate' options between acute and long-term care.

Rise in emergency admissions

66. Pressure on acute care has been growing, partly because of a rise in emergency admissions – particularly emergency medical admissions. It is evident from the literature, and from local reviews, that the causes of this rise are complex. But the result is that older people are increasingly being admitted to hospital and are using hospital services more: in 1994, 18 per cent of the population aged 75 plus were hospital inpatients at some time during the year, compared with 13 per cent in 1982 – an increasing proportion of an increasing population (Ref. 2).

EXHIBIT 21

Rebalancing services

Social services departments and health authorities need to plan services together.

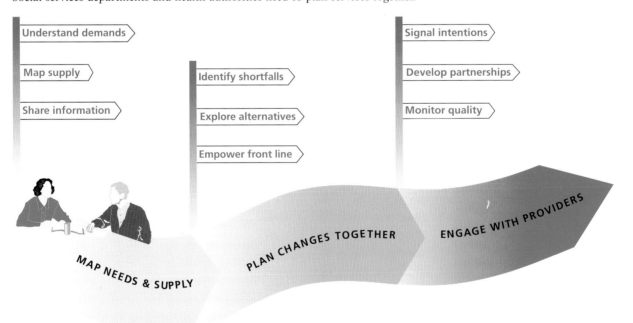

Understand demands

Map supply

Share information

Identify shortfalls

Explore alternatives

Empower front line

Signal intentions

Develop partnerships

Monitor quality

MAP NEEDS & SUPPLY

PLAN CHANGES TOGETHER

ENGAGE WITH PROVIDERS

Source: Audit Commission

EXHIBIT 22

Length of stay in the geriatric specialty

From 1989/90 to 1994/95 the average length of hospital stay in the geriatric specialty fell by 45 per cent.

Source: Department of Health (DoH) NHS Hospital Activity Statistics: England 1985 to 1995/96, Bulletin 1996/23, October 1996

Average length of stay (days)

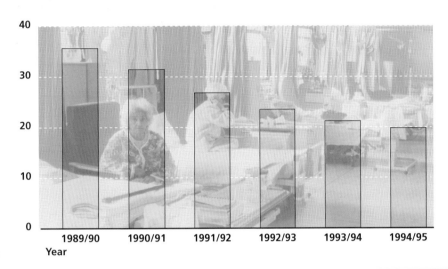

Shorter lengths of stay

67. Given these increases in admission rates, acute hospitals have been encouraged to reduce lengths of stay and thereby increase throughput. For example, over the five years from 1989/90 to 1994/95, the average length of stay in the geriatric specialty fell by 45 per cent – from 36 to 20 days [**EXHIBIT 22**]. Similar decreases have occurred in other specialties.

68. Shorter lengths of stay make it harder to plan discharge properly. But after their treatment, people still need somewhere to go. Most want to return home, but may require a period of rehabilitation. The Commission's study of fractured neck of femur found that few hospitals organised this aspect of care well, especially for people who need more time (Ref. 20). As a result, there are often discharge delays for people who still need some help, even though they may no longer need acute care. Rehabilitation can be organised at home successfully, but some people may need intensive support if they are to regain their confidence after a spell in hospital, and an intermediate facility may be required.

Lack of alternative options

69. Throughout the 1980s and early 1990s, the increasing pressures on acute hospitals of rising emergency admissions and shorter lengths of stay, coupled with the ready availability of private residential and nursing home provision, may have encouraged a reduction of rehabilitation and recovery resources. As mentioned above, the 1980s saw a gradual reduction in the number of long-stay beds for older people. This development was in part to be welcomed, as many of the beds were in very poor premises, and hospitals are no place for people to live. But at least these beds provided a place for people to recover gradually; their reduction has, in turn, reduced the options available to the NHS.

...admission was often potentially avoidable ... but the lack of suitable local alternatives often meant that an acute bed was the only option.

70. One health authority purchaser, concerned at the remorseless pressure on acute beds, reviewed how appropriately they were being used – whether admission was avoidable and the length of stay appropriate [CASE STUDY 7]. The review revealed that admission was often potentially avoidable for older people, particularly those aged over 75, but the lack of suitable local alternatives often meant that an acute bed was the only option [EXHIBIT 23]. Patients often needed 'institutionalised care but at a lower level than an expensive acute hospital – for example, care of the elderly, rehabilitation or community hospital with some on-site medical cover'. The level of need was apparent, but the most appropriate care was not available and in this context the admission was understandable.

CASE STUDY 7

Review of appropriateness of admission and stay in an acute hospital

Concern over pressure on beds and the high rate of emergency medical admissions led one health authority to review bed use.

The health authority applied the Appropriateness Evaluation Protocol (AEP) to care of the elderly and general medicine beds (and subsequently to general surgery) across two major acute NHS trusts in the city. The AEP was developed at the Boston University School of Medicine in 1981 and its use and development is well documented and evaluated [Ref. 21]. The AEP has been adapted for use in the UK [Ref. 22].

Prior to the review of bed use using the AEP, the prevailing view at the hospitals was:

> 'We need a new acute ward every 18 months to cope with the workload.'

> 'Every admission is appropriate, and every patient in a bed needs to be there.'

> 'We have done lots of studies, and we just need more beds.'

The review revealed that a considerable number of beds are being used for other than acute medical patients and that any increase in resources to cope should therefore be focused towards step-down facilities rather than more acute beds. It concluded that the *'key issue is the lack of step-down facilities for those patients who no longer have the need for acute hospital services'*.

It was recognised and acknowledged that the AEP is an academic tool and that in the real world 100 per cent appropriateness is totally unrealistic. It was noted that the 'current reality is that hospitals have no option but to accept patients and GPs have no option but to send their patients to acute hospitals. This means that all admissions are appropriate and all patients in a bed need to be there for one reason or another. This is because there are no alternative facilities where these patients can be managed.' However, the use of the AEP has begun to highlight how to start to change the situation. The results mean that the *'focus of the debate has changed completely. There is widespread recognition that more acute beds are not the solution. The debate is much wider than that, including the provision of step-down beds; the role of assessment units... and the relationship with social services.'*

EXHIBIT 23

Admissions to acute beds

...were often potentially avoidable for older people, particularly those aged over 75...

...but this was largely due to a lack of alternatives locally.

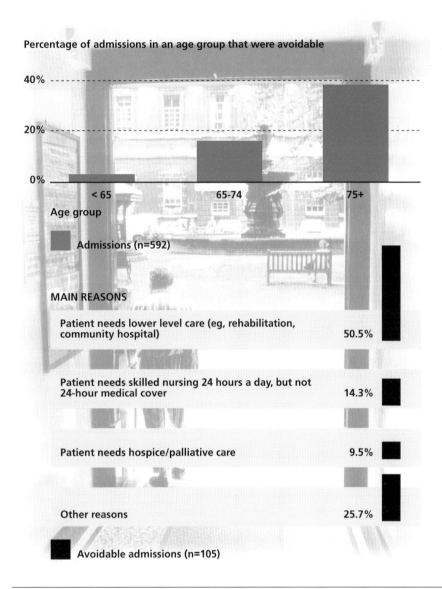

Percentage of admissions in an age group that were avoidable

Age group

■ Admissions (n=592)

MAIN REASONS

Patient needs lower level care (eg, rehabilitation, community hospital)	50.5%
Patient needs skilled nursing 24 hours a day, but not 24-hour medical cover	14.3%
Patient needs hospice/palliative care	9.5%
Other reasons	25.7%

■ Avoidable admissions (n=105)

Source: Two hospitals in a major city

71. The review also revealed that not only were older people more likely to have avoidable admissions, but they were also likely to stay longer than was necessary [**EXHIBIT 24, overleaf**]. The main reasons were poor discharge planning and management (already described in Chapter 1), but also, once again, a shortage of alternative facilities, described locally as 'step-down' facilities. Similar conclusions were reached in another acute hospital where a review found that, of those people who did not need to be in hospital, those requiring 'convalescence' or recovery were the largest group [**EXHIBIT 25, overleaf**]. These figures imply that length of stay in acute hospitals can be further reduced provided that suitable alternative care can be made available.

EXHIBIT 24

Inappropriate length of stay in two acute hospitals

Inappropriate stay worsened significantly with age.

Note: Days of stay (n=594)

Source: Two hospitals in a major city

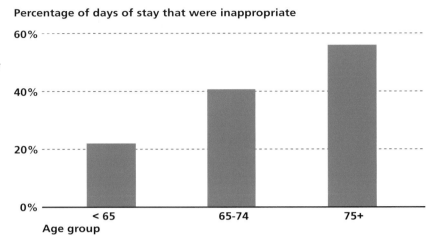

Percentage of days of stay that were inappropriate

Age group

EXHIBIT 25

Inappropriate length of stay in another acute hospital

Of those people who did not need to be in hospital, those requiring 'convalescence' or recovery were the largest group.

Source: Audit Commission fieldwork

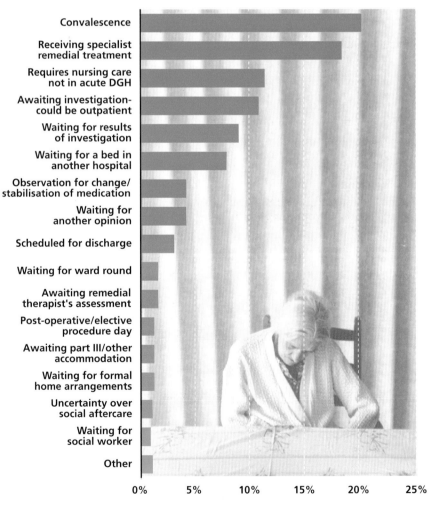

Main reason

- Convalescence
- Receiving specialist remedial treatment
- Requires nursing care not in acute DGH
- Awaiting investigation- could be outpatient
- Waiting for results of investigation
- Waiting for a bed in another hospital
- Observation for change/ stabilisation of medication
- Waiting for another opinion
- Scheduled for discharge
- Waiting for ward round
- Awaiting remedial therapist's assessment
- Post-operative/elective procedure day
- Awaiting part III/other accommodation
- Waiting for formal home arrangements
- Uncertainty over social aftercare
- Waiting for social worker
- Other

Percentage of total inappropriate bed days

Pressures on social services

72. Many acute hospitals are looking to social services to provide these intermediate care resources. But many social services departments feel ill equipped to cope as they, too, are under financial pressures.

73. From 1993 to 1996 general inflation has been 9 per cent and the population of the very elderly (85 plus) has increased by 14 per cent (Ref. 23). As mentioned in Chapter 1, central government made additional resources available through the special transitional grant (STG). But with the STG came increasing responsibilities and the baseline standard spending assessment (SSA net of the STG) has increased by just 1 per cent from 1993 to 1996. The SSA is merely indicative of the level of expenditure that the Government considers appropriate for social services. Each local authority can decide within total resources how much it is actually going to spend on social services. Most authorities have given priority to social services, spending more than the SSA [**EXHIBIT 26**]. In 1997/98 the average spend is 9 per cent above SSA (compared with 9 per cent above in 1996/97 and 7 per cent above in 1995/96), again reflecting the pressures that authorities are under (Ref. 24). However, it may become increasingly difficult for local authorities to sustain this level of spend as education becomes a priority.

74. The pattern that is emerging in social services departments is one of:

- continuing high use of nursing and residential home places;

- lower priority given to alternative services in the community; and

- in some cases, limits on the number of placements.

EXHIBIT 26

Percentage spend above or below SSA allocation for social services

In 1997/98 the average spend is 9 per cent above SSA.

Percentage spend above or below SSA

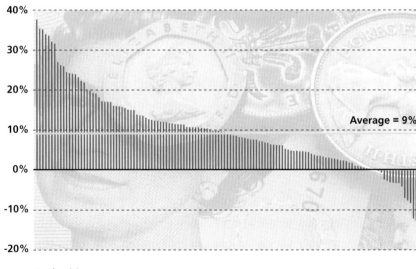

Average = 9%

Authorities

Source: CIPFA

Pressures to place in nursing and residential homes

75. One of the purposes of the 1990 NHS and Community Care Act was to rebalance expenditure between residential and nursing homes and care in people's own homes. In practice, while the growth in the number of publicly funded residents in residential and nursing homes has slowed, it has not declined. Those admitted prior to 1 April 1993 and funded by social security payments, and those admitted since and funded by local authorities, have increased in total by only 1 per cent between 1993 and 1996 (Ref. 25).

76. But in order to sustain this number of residents, social services departments are having to spend increasing amounts on nursing and residential care, which has reached, on average, 64 per cent of their funds [EXHIBIT 20, p34]. This national average disguises huge differences between individual areas. Some are spending considerable sums: the use of residential care standardised by age varies by a factor of six between authorities [EXHIBIT 27].

EXHIBIT 27

Use by social services departments of residential and nursing home care, 1996

Use varies by a factor of six.

Long-stay supported residents, per 1,000 75+ population at March 1996

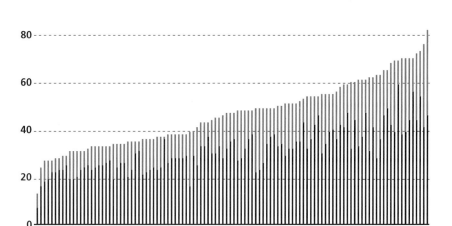

Source: DoH, Key Indicators Graphical System

77. A key factor influencing this pattern may well be the inheritance of authorities in 1993: the pattern of demand has been determined at least in part by readily available supply. Local authorities that are host to a larger number of nursing home places, for example, have more people from their area placed in nursing homes [EXHIBIT 28].

78. While it might be the case that supply has adjusted in response to demand, it is at least as likely to be the other way around. The additional funds made available to local authorities through the STG were subject to a constraint that 85 per cent be used on independent sector services: a ready supply of residential and nursing homes was at hand while independent sector home care was relatively underdeveloped.

79. Another factor contributing to the high numbers in care homes is the existence of a perverse financial incentive for authorities to use residential and nursing home care in preference to caring for people in their own homes. Charging frameworks take into account the capital released from the sale of people's property when they enter residential care and a residential allowance is available to individuals in independent sector homes. As a result, the Commission has already commented that in 'nearly all situations it is substantially cheaper for local authorities to place people in residential care, even where there is no difference between the gross cost of residential care and care at home' (Ref. 24).

EXHIBIT 28

Use and supply of nursing home care, March 1996

Where supply is higher, use by the local authority is also higher.

Long-stay supported residents ÷ 1,000 population aged 75+

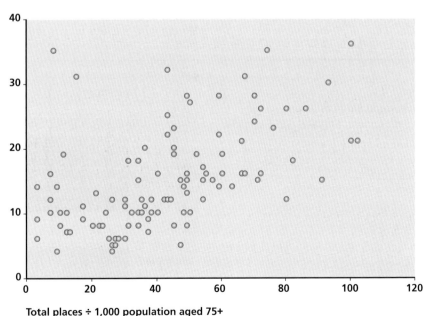

Total places ÷ 1,000 population aged 75+

Source: DoH, Key Indicators Graphical System

Lower priority to alternative services

80. Use of home care has also increased since 1993, but not as quickly as that on residential and nursing homes [EXHIBIT 29]. The average also conceals wide variations: 22 authorities actually decreased home help hours from 1993 to 1996, and the number of social services departments that reduce home care hours also increased annually. Data are available for all years for 89 authorities – of these, 12 (14 per cent) reduced the level of home care available in 1994 from 1993, 35 (39 per cent) in 1995 from 1994, and 40 (45 per cent) in 1996 from 1995 (Ref. 26).

Limits on the number of placements

81. High placement numbers result in high costs. Many social services departments are experiencing problems in continuing to meet the demands placed upon them; with the transfer of resources through the STG drawing to an end, a number of authorities are running short of resources to fund new placements or packages of care.

82. One authority found that it had to limit the number of placements in 1996/97 to below the historical trend, which led to increasing delays [EXHIBIT 30]. Many of the individuals waiting for places were in hospital, and so limiting the number of placements delayed their discharge. This meant that patients continued to occupy acute beds unnecessarily. Another authority projected in its 1997/98 budget that 'at least 200 older people will not be funded in nursing or residential care' who would have been in 1996/97. This trend is resulting in older people being placed in effect on a 'waiting list' – awaiting funding for placement. Another authority had a substantial waiting list, including large numbers awaiting placement in nursing homes from hospital [EXHIBIT 31].

EXHIBIT 29

Increase in services arranged by social services, England 1992 to 1996

Use of nursing and residential care has increased at a faster rate than use of home care.

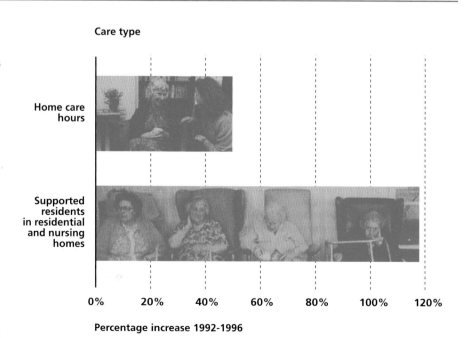

Care type

Home care hours

Supported residents in residential and nursing homes

0% 20% 40% 60% 80% 100% 120%

Percentage increase 1992-1996

Source: DoH, Community Care Statistics, 1996; Residential Accommodation Statistics, 1996

EXHIBIT 30

Social services budget difficulties – placements in nursing homes

One authority had to limit the number of placements in 1996/97, below the historical trend, leading to the creation of a waiting list.

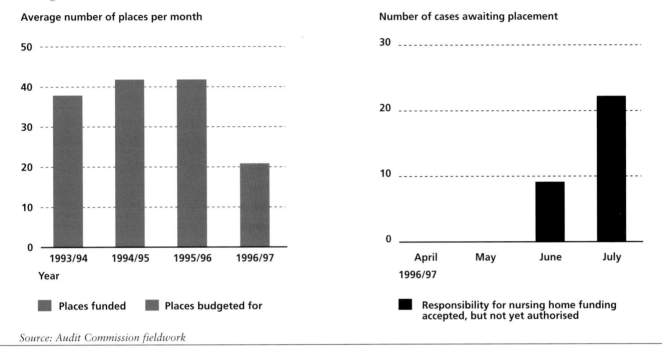

Average number of places per month

Number of cases awaiting placement

Places funded   Places budgeted for

Responsibility for nursing home funding accepted, but not yet authorised

Source: Audit Commission fieldwork

EXHIBIT 31

Waiting list for nursing home care

Another authority had a substantial waiting list, including large numbers awaiting placement in nursing homes from hospital.

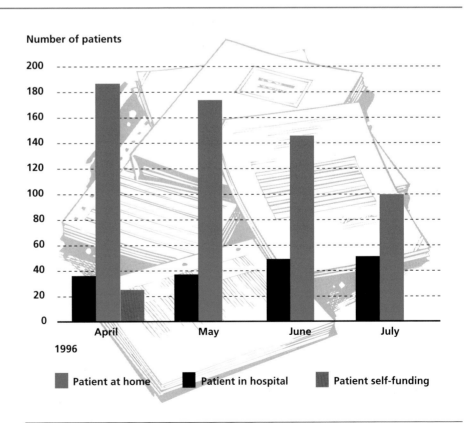

Number of patients

1996

Patient at home   Patient in hospital   Patient self-funding

Source: Audit Commission fieldwork

...pressures on the NHS and social services departments are combining to create a vicious circle.

83. Social services departments are becoming increasingly concerned at the level of demand they face following hospital discharge, which is also effectively limiting their ability to provide support to people still in the community who need it. The Association of Metropolitan Authorities stated that an 'increase in demand for an intensity of service for a few people with a high level of personal care needs will mean that very many people who require less intense service packages will receive no service at all. Seven clients receiving a service that costs less than £20 a week have to stop receiving services in order for a client to receive a community care package of £140 a week within a limited budget. This is described as the 'gearing effect' (Ref. 27). Thus, high-level need drives out those with less – but often substantial – need.

The vicious circle

84. All these pressures on the NHS and social services departments are combining to create a vicious circle [EXHIBIT 32].

85. The pressure on expensive hospital beds and the high use of residential and nursing homes is making it hard to free up resources for alternative services that might start to ease the situation. Investment in rehabilitation and convalescent facilities to follow an acute hospital episode on the one hand, and in services reducing the need for hospital admissions on the other, could provide a more cost-effective strategy. But to implement such a change of direction requires:

- joint working to map services and plan how to rebalance them; and
- development of a wider range of options.

Joint working

86. The NHS and social services departments are locked together in the vicious circle. Although action by each agency is essential, action by one alone will not be enough. Their inter-dependence needs to be recognised if proper progress is to be made. If one agency tries to break the circle on its own by investing in alternative services, it is likely to relieve the pressure on the other immediately but will only benefit itself in the long term. For example, if hospitals invest in more beds or facilities for rehabilitation, this will relieve the pressure on social services for residential and nursing homes. Similarly, if social services invest in effective preventative services such as respite care and intensive support at home for short periods during a crisis, then hospitals could benefit from fewer emergency admissions. Preventive services that stop admissions are also likely to require more investment in primary care for the active management of chronic conditions. Similarly, housing departments have a major role to play in ensuring access to good quality housing to allow people to be cared for in their own homes. Joint planning and commissioning are therefore essential to explore alternative services.

EXHIBIT 32

The vicious circle

The pressure on expensive hospital beds and the high use of nursing and residential homes is making it hard to free up resources for alternative services that might start to ease the situation.

87. There are preliminary indications that, where services are in a better balance, the circle can be broken [CASE STUDY 8]. For example, the pattern of care for older people in Area B, which has no delayed discharges, contrasts with that in Area A, which has a high number of delayed discharges.

CASE STUDY 8

Continuing care arrangements in two different areas

Area A spends significantly above its SSA and has a gross spend per head on older people of three times that of Area B... And yet beds are blocked in A...

	AREA A Very long waiting lists	AREA B No waiting lists or blocked beds
Social services position relative to SSA	Significantly above	Below
Social services gross spend on older people's services/ pop. 75 plus	£1,600+	£600+

Area A also supports more people in homes and has a higher admission rate.

Social services – supported residential and nursing home placements/ 1,000 aged 75 plus	54	41
Social services monthly nursing home admission rate/ 1,000 75 plus	1.9	0.8
Nursing home places available/1,000 75 plus	95	52

In Area B there are more continuing care beds, more rehabilitation beds, and the health authority has a lower readmission rate.

Health authority continuing care beds for older people/ 1,000 75 plus	0.8	1.8
Health authority continuing care beds for rehabilitation/ 1,000 75 plus	2.6	4.9
Health authority readmission rate – for people aged 75 plus within 90 days	20%	13%

Moreover in Area B there is more investment in the community and joint working between health and social services.

Social services intensive home care packages: per cent 6+ visits per week	26%	39%
Percentage of care packages that are multidisciplinary	3%	49%
Health authority: per cent spend on community services	8%	10%

While such structural solutions might help, a focus for joint working, shared priorities and shared procedures could achieve just as much.

88. The socio-economic characteristics of the two areas are different and some of the variation in the use of residential and nursing home care is probably explained by poorer housing and the need for local authority A to support a greater proportion of the population, while some people in B might be expected to fund their own care. But this factor alone is unlikely to explain a use of nursing home care in A nearly three times as great as in B, while in A – where they are more likely to be needed – there are half the number of rehabilitation beds as in B. The more likely explanation is that the pressures on Area A have prevented some of the initiatives in Area B.

Working together

89. While the need for health and social services to work ever more closely together is widely acknowledged, the practicalities of doing so can be very difficult. Recent reorganisation in local government and mergers between health authorities have left few sharing common boundaries or serving common populations. Cultures remain different, with health, for example, having a universal and social services a targeted service. And even the sharing of electronic data about people can be difficult as the law protects privacy even though both health and social services are helping the same person.

90. Increasingly, these difficulties have led many to call for a single agency to manage the task. While this would eliminate the interface between the two agencies, it could cause other problems, such as increased bureaucracy, and would require a realignment of political accountability.

91. A possible compromise might be to grant powers to both agencies to set up a joint agency with a single chief executive, to whom both health and social services would delegate authority and finance. Such a joint agency would commission care for older people for a specific geographical area – which might be the area common to both agencies – with a single pooled budget. It would be accountable to both (or to all if more than two authorities are involved). But here again there are risks of bureaucracy and the creation of further interfaces. Whatever solution is proposed, it must be with a view to improving cost-effectiveness and outcomes for older people.

92. While such structural solutions might help, a focus for joint working, shared priorities and shared procedures could achieve just as much. Reference has already been made to the need for agreement on responsibilities for people being discharged from hospital. Agreements, guidelines and protocols would clarify who is expected to do what. They might also clarify expectations for potential users and their carers; but they also lock agencies into providing services even when the money runs out. All schemes would need to be costed and revised if financial pressures on one agency turn out to be greater than expected.

EXHIBIT 33

Health authorities' work on continuing care

Many policies and criteria are not based on continuing care needs mapping or even a clear identification of the current number of beds available.

Percentage of authorities

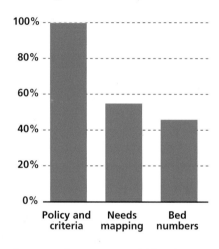

Source: Audit Commission fieldwork

EXHIBIT 34

Social services information on demand coming to them via hospitals

Only a minority of social services departments record the demand that they face from hospital.

Number of social services departments

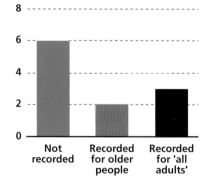

Source: Audit Commission fieldwork

93. The best way forward is not yet clear. An experimental approach is needed to evaluate different options. While the Government's recently announced 'health action zones' (HAZs) provide one such opportunity, radical approaches cannot be explored without changes in legislation. There is, however, much that authorities can do now. They can start by taking stock of their current range of services and identifying where the pressure points are, before going on to develop a wider range of complementary services.

Service mapping

94. This sort of stocktake needs to be done by agencies together as the first step in working out how to rebalance services. Health authorities, trusts and social services need to start by sharing information openly and reviewing the pattern of care locally. Doing this in practice can help to reveal patterns like the one in Case Study 8, which starts to point to possible ways of rebalancing services.

95. Many health authorities have only a partial picture of local arrangements; policies and criteria are rarely based on any mapping of continuing care needs or even a clear identification of the current number of beds available [**EXHIBIT 33**]. Whether or not policies translate into services for older people is a matter of chance as a result.

96. The first step in mapping is a review of current arrangements. Without this information, it is difficult to see how health commissioners can have full confidence in continuing care arrangements. Dorset Health Authority has carried out a range of reviews and analysis to help ensure that its policies and criteria are robust, and to identify areas for change. This series of reviews helped to quantify provision, its distribution, use, appropriateness, and areas where change is necessary [**CASE STUDY 9**].

97. Social services must also review what they are doing. They depend heavily on the health sector for demand and the independent care sector for supply. And yet their understanding of the demands from health are poor: only a minority of social services departments are recording the demand that they face from hospitals systematically [**EXHIBIT 34**]. They need this information so that they can sit down with health managers and work out the resources for the placements and packages of care needed, challenging the figures where levels appear to be high to see if alternatives are possible. Where health authorities are themselves failing to map needs, this process becomes all the more difficult for local authorities.

CASE STUDY 9

Development of continuing care policy and eligibility criteria

Dorset Health Authority, in developing its continuing healthcare policy and eligibility criteria for implementation in April 1996, reviewed the following information to develop a comprehensive service map:

- number of NHS inpatient continuing healthcare, rehabilitation, and respite care beds by provider and by care group (for example, older people and older people with severe mental illness);

- average lengths of stay for inpatient continuing healthcare, rehabilitation, and respite care beds by provider and care group;

- percentage occupancy for inpatient continuing healthcare, rehabilitation, and respite care wards by provider and care group;

- community health staff numbers and specialism; and

- comparison with other health authorities – for example, in terms of numbers of inpatient continuing healthcare beds for older people and older people with severe mental illness, and community nurses, using health service indicators and regional data.

Using the matrix recommended by the NHS Executive, the authority also costed continuing healthcare provision by service (as per Annex A of HSG (95) 8), setting (hospital, nursing home, community, etc) and client group.

It then used this information to make judgements about:

- the overall level of NHS continuing healthcare provision in Dorset;

- the appropriateness of that level of provision (for example, in terms of its location – hospital or community);

- whether there were 'gaps' in provision;

- service levels in different geographical locations within the county; and

- the areas where future action would be required (for example, to changes in service levels or type).

A comprehensive document was developed setting out the purchasing implications of the continuing healthcare policy, with a detailed discussion of the implications for the services for each client group.

98. Social services record even less about the services that people receive after discharge from hospital (for example, the proportion of placements to nursing homes or residential homes from each local hospital). Such information would seem to be essential for any dialogue between health and social services if the hospital/continuing care/ community care interface is to be managed effectively. As the Commission commented in *Balancing the Care Equation* (Ref. 24) local authorities must improve their information. In addition, in the 1997 Annual Report of the Joint Reviews states that for 'services to keep improving, better information systems and better use of information already collected are essential' (Ref. 17).

RECOMMENDATION

Health authorities and trusts should review whether older people are currently being admitted to hospital beds because alternative services are not available and identify what alternative services are needed. They should then agree common priorities with social services.

...allowing care managers to manage entire budgets and learning from how they spend them ... provides a more reliable source of information for matching services to needs.

99. Just as for health, mapping the market should start to enable social services to identify general trends and shortfalls in provision [CASE STUDY 10]. However, they also need to be responsive to information fed back from providers, service users and their care managers. The authority centre can then endeavour to commission services to fill any gaps identified. In one-half of fieldwork authorities there were mechanisms to feed back information about potential service gaps to the centre, although for legal reasons many authorities are cautious about recording any information concerning service shortfalls – even to provide internal information for development. Other authorities either did not record shortfalls or introduced focus groups or planning forums instead. But allowing care managers to manage entire budgets and learning from how they spend them, as described in Chapter 2, provides a more reliable source of information for matching services to needs.

100. Cornwall County Council carried out a one-month survey of hospital discharges. By looking at people, rather than counting services, this survey showed that the workload was not all 'new' demand. It also revealed the importance not just of the workload and its nature, but of total numbers and dispersion [CASE STUDY 11].

CASE STUDY 10

Market mapping – two examples

Kensington and Chelsea Social Services Department has conducted a borough-wide service mapping exercise of needs and services for older people. It adopted a 'rapid-appraisal' market research technique to survey current service users and older people in the community at large. It also mapped all of their provision by geographic area. Recent analysis of the research has enabled the borough to identify how well services meet the needs of the community. This has identified undersupply in areas such as daycare and carer support. The research has also raised issues over the quality of home care provision.

Westminster Social Services Department conducts market reviews on an ongoing basis, starting with user consultation and specifying services. Its central contracts unit then meets with key provider organisations from time to time to gain an understanding of the capabilities of providers to undertake the plans of the authority. Over time the unit has observed changes in the maturity of the market and is now more confident in using the independent sector for services such as provision for people with learning disabilities.

CASE STUDY 11

Study of hospital referrals to social services

Cornwall Social Services Department carried out a special study of all hospital discharges for one month where social services were involved. This showed that:

- there were 250 discharges from hospitals across the county;

- they were from 26 different hospitals;

- discharges from six acute hospitals accounted for 65 per cent (162 cases) of all discharges; and

- the remaining 35 per cent (88 cases) were from 20 community and care of the elderly hospitals spread throughout the county – an average of four discharges per month per hospital.

A more detailed analysis was carried out on a sample of 107 of the 250 cases drawn from the area which deals with the largest number of hospital discharges in the county. This showed that:

- 61 per cent (65 cases) were existing social services clients;

- 58 per cent (62 cases) were given a service, of which 18 cases were new and 44 cases were re-starts or modifications to existing care packages; and

- after three months, 41 people were still receiving services (around two-thirds of those originally given a service).

101. Mapping of needs and services should then lead to the planning of the overall direction of change. This should in turn allow both health and social services to start putting in place new initiatives to rebalance services. This can be difficult.

RECOMMENDATION

Health authorities and social services departments should map needs and the services available to meet them. They should share this information with each other as the basis for joint planning and commissioning. Social services should review their spending patterns, use of residential and nursing homes, use of home care, any limits to placements, and make adjustments to this mix where needed. Health and social services authorities should support their mapping processes by introducing information systems that allow them to update their maps on a regular basis.

...if authorities are to change the pattern of service provision, they need to develop imaginative alternatives.

102. The commissioning of services that already exist is relatively straightforward – the products and their costs are well known and purchasers merely need to enshrine current practices in service agreements, or in contracts with large suppliers like hospitals or homes. However, if authorities are to change the pattern of service provision, they need to develop imaginative alternatives. An approach that increases investment in preventative approaches and intermediate facilities will need to rely increasingly on the initiative and innovation of local practitioners. This approach is more complex, replacing institutional providers with a more flexible network of services in the community. The role of the centre remains just as important – but it changes in nature.

103. Instead of purchasing directly, the centres must work together with the other agencies involved to shape the overall environment within which local practitioners can work. At the same time, they must create an environment in which providers feel sufficiently secure to invest in new services and aim for higher standards. To achieve both objectives at once requires more sophisticated relationships with providers and contracting mechanisms.

Developing health services

104. Health authorities must start to decide what changes are needed and what gaps need to be bridged. Many have already started introducing imaginative initiatives. Some are trying to reduce admissions to hospital by providing care in different ways, through focused, community-based schemes. The Elderly Persons Integrated Care System (EPICS) in Marlow offers an alternative system of integrated care in the community for people aged 65 and over, who are resident in the Marlow area, and might otherwise be admitted to hospital [CASE STUDY 12].

105. The scheme was built around close working between GPs, the primary healthcare team and secondary healthcare. Support for GPs and closer links with secondary healthcare professionals and social services are essential. Only the availability of such input as in Case Study 12 will give GPs the support needed to reduce unnecessary admissions to hospital. Another health authority has established a scheme to prevent admission, which:

- requires social services to 'maintain input' on existing service levels;
- makes available a small cash budget to enable additional social care to be purchased, to prevent more expensive healthcare; and
- makes available additional support from geriatricians for home visits.

CASE STUDY 12

Elderly Persons Integrated Care System

The Elderly Persons Integrated Care System (EPICS) in Marlow, Buckinghamshire aims to maintain people in the community by providing flexible, responsive packages of care according to assessed needs, placing particular emphasis on speed of response to prevent inappropriate admissions to hospital in times of crisis. EPICS aims to:

- provide easily accessible information;
- provide a single point of access 24 hours a day;
- co-ordinate assessment to ensure the best possible package of support for clients and carers; and, most importantly
- provide at short notice an EPICS care worker with a flexible package of short or out-of-hours visiting, overnight and 24-hour support.

The scheme is built around GP practices. A co-ordinator and project manager are accountable to the elderly care directorate of South Buckinghamshire NHS Trust. The board of management has senior management representatives from health, social services and the voluntary sector.

The system has been evaluated and costed. In a GP satisfaction survey, 12 out of 15 GPs said that EPICS intervention had prevented admission to hospital , while three felt that it had not. In 31 detailed client interviews, over two-thirds expressed the view that they would hope to access EPICS again if a similar situation occurred in the future. In a review of 66 referrers' views by questionnaire, 87 per cent said that the service had provided what had been needed for their client, with 88 per cent reporting EPICS response as timely.

The system manages the interface between primary and secondary care, health and social services. The average length of intervention by EPICS is 7.5 days, with an average input of 15.6 hours from the EPICS care workers (average cost £308). An audit was carried out to assess the potential utility of EPICS as an alternative to patients who were admitted to hospital, resident in the authority area over a five-month period (January to May 1996). The audit revealed that in all, 51 episodes out of 331 (15 per cent) could have been helped, either by reducing length of stay by facilitating earlier discharge (23 cases, saving 197 bed days), or by preventing admission (28 cases, saving 367 bed days). Costings show that, assuming from the five-month data that 123 patients could have been helped by EPICS in a year, this would save 1,354 bed days for more appropriate use. After allowing for the cost of EPICS input, just under £220,000 could potentially be saved and redirected to other services.

A continuously updated client database and a database of available services are central to the operation of the system. Development funding has been provided through joint finance, and operational resources through the elderly care directorate of the trust.

106. A number of health commissioners have recognised the need to improve community health services to enhance the options for older people outside of hospital – both prior to admission and on discharge. However, the contracting currency – numbers of contacts – is a very poor measure. Purchasing another 5,000 district nurse or physiotherapy contacts to improve services is an act of faith. Some health authorities are working with community providers to ensure that community services are better targeted and provide value for money. For example, one healthcare trust has carried out a comprehensive analysis and weighting exercise for all types of intervention and activity normally carried out by every

Rehabilitation is currently advocated by many as 'the missing factor' in the care of elderly people.

community discipline [CASE STUDY 13]. This helps to form the basis of a scoring mechanism for caseload management. Another authority, concerned at 'caseload'-led demand management has, with a local NHS trust, produced eligibility criteria for all community health services [CASE STUDY 14]. These are useful developments for ensuring that maximum and appropriate benefit is derived from community health services.

107. Rehabilitation is currently advocated by many as 'the missing factor' in the care of elderly people. What is clear is that many health authorities lack basic knowledge about the rehabilitation services for older people in their area. This lack of information must be addressed. The Audit Commission will be reviewing arrangements for rehabilitation in detail over the next 18 months.

CASE STUDY 13

District nursing workload activity

Cornwall Community Healthcare Trust was continually frustrated at the contract currency (contacts) in use for measuring community activity. It was felt that with advances in technology and faster turnover in acute settings, community services are now dealing with a far more complex range of patient care and treatment needs. Numbers of face-to-face contacts alone are felt to be meaningless and misleading.

The Trust carried out a comprehensive analysis and weighting exercise for all types of intervention and activity normally carried out by every community discipline. This analysis has revealed the caseload breakdown by:

- problem (for example, leg ulcers, wound care, etc);
- nurse grade; and
- activity (for example, face-to-face work, non-face-to-face work, travel time, etc).

For instance, it is now known that within the Trust, 13 per cent of staff time in total is spent travelling and 48 per cent of time in face-to-face contact with patients, the biggest component of workload being leg ulcers, cancer and wound care. Locally, managers can now judge the appropriateness of their percentages overall and by nurse grade.

The data will form the basis of a caseload scoring mechanism that will be used to identify when an individual caseload has reached its manageable maximum.

Finally, linked work has examined and identified baseline costings for nursing activities in order to inform the contract process.

CASE STUDY 14

Eligibility criteria for community health services

Bromley Health Authority and a local NHS trust have produced eligibility criteria for community health services. The health authority saw the need to develop eligibility criteria to avoid 'caseload'-led demand management. Criteria have been developed for referral, assessment and treatment for:

- district nursing;
- adult physiotherapy;
- adult occupational therapy;
- adult speech and language therapy;
- chiropody;
- community dietetic services; and
- wheelchair services.

For example, for district nursing services, three categories and five dependency levels are used:

Category A: complex/multi-need	Level 5: maximum care
	Level 4: above average care
Category B: moderate/shared care	Level 3: average care
Category C: advisory/minimal	Level 2: minimal care
	Level 1: self-care

Caseloads are then monitored monthly against the categories, by:

- service (for example, general nursing, specialist nursing);
- age group (for example, adult or children);
- location (for example, nursing home, residential home, patient's home); and
- individual service user.

Supporting primary care

...new partnerships between primary and secondary care may make good sense.

108. These sorts of initiatives are likely to put increasing pressures on primary care and GP services at a time when many are already under pressure. Rather than leave GPs to carry the burden, new partnerships between primary and secondary care may make good sense. A number of options [BOX B, overleaf] was recently put forward in an editorial in the *British Medical Journal* (Ref. 28).

BOX B

Options proposed to support primary care

1. Visiting medical officers could be appointed specifically to provide the medical management of nursing homes.

2. Geriatric medical and psychiatric outreach services could be set up. Hospital departments would become responsible for the routine surveillance and management of people in nursing homes with primary care consortiums covering out of hours.

3. Shared medical care could be established with increased input from hospital staff through visiting and advice.

4. Integrated medical care could be organised. Primary care would retain responsibility, with service payments for medical assessments on admission and for reviews. Geriatric services would provide structured support through the development of care management programmes. According to the authors, option 4 has many attractions.

5. Health maintenance organisations could be set up with nursing homes employing their own medical staff on their own terms.

Forthcoming guidance ... will increase the freedom allowed to health authorities to experiment...

109. Forthcoming guidance from the NHS Executive will increase the freedom allowed to health authorities to experiment with alternatives: either through Primary Care Act pilots for personal medical services or through section 36 of the Act, which allows certain authorities to use hospital and community health services funding to develop quality enhancements in primary care together with GPs.

110. It may be that a number of options should be tried and evaluated on an experimental basis. Some GPs and primary care teams would be keen to take on a leading role; others might welcome active support from elderly care physicians. The financing of different options would need to be considered carefully to reflect different responsibilities. Should secondary care teams take over responsibility for older people and hold 'lists' of patients as GPs do, or be assigned the proportion of the fund that would otherwise go to fundholders? Should older people themselves be able to choose between a GP and a specialist to manage their care?

111. Whatever options are adopted, it is essential that primary care practitioners should feel confident of support if care in the community is to increase. Close links with social services are essential and these can be established at the operational level through care managers, as described in the previous chapter. But care managers also need to be provided with the right environment, and approaches for doing this are outlined in the next section.

RECOMMENDATION

Health authorities should work with trusts to develop new forms of provision to reduce admissions to hospital by providing care in alternative ways, and to explore ways of improving rehabilitation after treatment where appropriate.

Developing social services

112. The challenges facing social services are different from those facing the health service. In order to explore alternatives to current services patterns, authorities need to empower service users and care managers, as described in Chapter 2. But in itself this is not sufficient: they also need to ensure that conditions are conducive to developing innovative services. The development of close relationships with providers is all the more important since over half their expenditure on provision is now with external suppliers (Ref. 29).

113. The model of commissioners and providers working closely together towards common goals has been widely promoted. Businesses such as Marks & Spencer and Motorola have been studied for the benefits that have flowed from this approach, such as customer-responsiveness and cost-effectiveness (Ref. 30). The nature of community care – a service provided to vulnerable clients who are often in a secluded environment – makes partnerships essential. The following benefits should accrue from a close working relationship:

- reduced risk of a poor quality service and of the need for monitoring;
- greater potential for innovation, since the expertise of both commissioners and providers is harnessed;
- reduced transaction costs through streamlining;
- reduced marketing costs for providers; and
- some real incentives for providers to improve standards.

114. But to develop effectiveness, these relationships need to demonstrate the following qualities:

- transparency;
- accountability;
- openness;
- trust; and
- sustainability.

Interviews with independent providers suggested that these characteristics are not always present and identified frustration with some social services departments. In one authority a residential homeowner described how he had been led by the authority to believe that more elderly dementia care provision was needed. After investing considerable sums in a new home, the provider discovered that the authority had run out of funds and could not make any referrals. With such broken promises partnerships are unlikely to last. Below is a summary of the feedback given by independent sector providers [BOX C].

BOX C

Independent sector provider concerns and suggestions

CONCERNS	SUGGESTIONS
Information/access	
• Need to share problems with providers, not to impose changes or cuts without consultation	• Need to share information on changes in strategy that will affect providers
• Often insufficient contact with key purchasing staff; often difficult to address issues due to size and infrequency of forums and absence of relevant staff	• More regular forums of a reasonable size, possibly area-based, and more informal contacts at different levels of the organisation
Culture/attitude	
• Belief that users are not always given a choice of provider	• Need for authorities to enable informed choice and demonstrate that users are making choices
• Feeling that local authority or not-for-profit providers are favoured over the private sector	• Open and measurable criteria about how authorities choose providers, and application of these criteria to providers in all sectors
• Need to trust the independent sector to build a relationship	• Greater pursuit of innovative schemes with contracts that offer more security for providers and better services for local authorities
Strategic planning	
• Need for more forward planning – longer-term purchasing plans, not summaries of decisions already taken	• Longer-term community care plans, with more financial information
• Not enough risk-sharing – authorities are not willing to experiment with different contract types	• Need to explore benefits to both purchasers and providers of a wider range of contracts
• Need for more clarity around the boundaries of purchaser/provider (and other) monitoring roles	• Monitoring strategies that reflect the fact that providers are front-line, and can naturally do some monitoring more effectively
Operations	
• Lack of prompt payment in some authorities	• Some authorities have direct debit; others have opted for standard invoicing
• Paperwork is unwieldy; for example, specifications are too legalistic and input-focused	• More outcome-focused specifications, greater reliance on partnership, less focus on the contract
• Some tendering applications are bureaucratic, ask for unnecessary information and do not state selection criteria	• More open and standard tendering procedures in keeping with best practice authorities

115. In order to develop better relationships with external providers, authorities need to be more even-handed. This requires an understanding of how service providers are motivated and a willingness to meet them half way. The key areas to address are to:

- develop contracting and funding mechanisms that reward providers for quality and innovation;

- improve working relationships with external providers to make transactions more efficient; and

- monitor the quality of *all* provision to ensure that delivery is of the appropriate standard.

Funding and contracting mechanisms

116. In its last community care bulletin the Commission commented on the adverse effects of separate accounting for external and local authority provision (Ref. 24).

'Most authorities account separately for the Special Transitional Grant (STG) and base budget monies. Instead, resources need to be managed in an integrated way and merged into a single commissioning budget. The current arrangements are leading to two sets of services, with the bulk being provided by local authorities and funded directly from the centre and the remainder being provided by the independent sector and purchased independently by care managers through the STG.'

117. Fieldwork for this report found that local authority provider budgets were still funded directly and managed separately in three-quarters of authorities. Under such a system, care managers' ability to influence local authority providers and therefore shape the pattern of service provision is reduced, since providers receive their funds directly from the centre. The direct funding of local authority provision also results in the need for the 'in-house first' policies mentioned in Chapter 2. These are an attempt to make full use of the resources that authorities have already committed, rather than to allow care managers the flexibility to commit those resources themselves. This is likely to constrain innovation.

118. By contrast, the purchasing (often called STG) budget is held by care managers. Spot purchasing[I] is still almost universally adopted for the independent sector. Only four out of ten fieldwork authorities use block or cost-and-volume contracts to purchase external services, and this is often for small-scale projects only or with former in-house providers [EXHIBIT 35, overleaf].

I   These include 'option-to-purchase' or 'call-off' contracts where the price – but no volume of service – is guaranteed, and thus the risk burden is still placed on the service provider.

EXHIBIT 35

Contract types for independent sector spend on elderly care, 1996/97

Spot purchasing is still almost universally adopted for the independent sector.

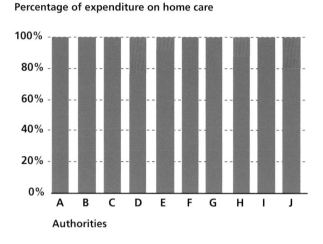

Percentage of expenditure on residential care

Percentage of expenditure on home care

Authorities

Authorities

■ Spot   ■ Other

Note: 'Other' includes block and cost and volume arrangements.
Source: Audit Commission fieldwork

119. The current pattern of provision is thus polarised between central direct funding for local authority services, and local spot purchasing for the independent sector, even though options exist in between [EXHIBIT 36].

120. Both direct funding and spot contracting offer advantages, but also considerable drawbacks: direct funding offers security and financial control for the authority, but makes services less flexible and responsive to the user; local spot purchasing maximises choice but often means high transaction costs and unhelpful instability for the provider. In effect, all the risk is borne by the provider and none by the purchaser, but service users may well suffer poorer quality services as a result.

EXHIBIT 36

Current local authority funding arrangements for provision

The norm is still for in-house services to be directly funded and external services to be spot-purchased.

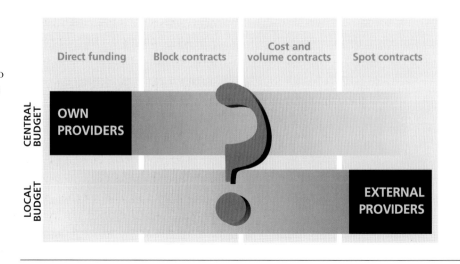

Source: Audit Commission

Authorities should be experimenting with options to find the right balance between security and flexibility.

121. Intermediate forms of contract offer some guarantee of volume for the provider. This can be more efficient: for example, one fieldwork authority saved £7 million on a budget of £70 million expenditure through making the majority of its purchases through a range of small and large block contracts. However, such agreements may not always yield cost savings; benefits may accrue in other ways. For example, more reliable services might be provided; or services might be able to cope with more dependent clients. One fieldwork authority decided to use block contracts to encourage the independent sector to provide rural home care, respite and daycare. It has since found that providers are willing to bid for work, which previously might not have been commercially viable for them to take on, if they are given some guarantee of demand.

122. But block contracts can have many of the disadvantages of central funding if not based on what older people want. Cost and volume contracts provide a minimum guaranteed volume for providers, which can be well within amounts purchased in previous years, but which gives providers some security. Above this minimum, care managers can 'call off' services at an agreed standard cost, giving them some flexibility. Authorities should be experimenting with options to find the right balance between security and flexibility.

123. In essence, the contracting approach should relate to the local market circumstances. For example, in the residential sector, where the *Direction on Choice* (allowing people to choose their own care home) constrains authorities, spot purchasing at least initially enables authorities to identify the unconstrained pattern of demand. However, it seems that authorities are also using this model for other services such as home care, where it may be less appropriate, as the market is still immature in many parts of the country. A full range of contract types is likely to be needed to encourage the market to develop or change. Market mapping should provide a basis for tailoring their contracting approach to influence the market in positive ways, rather than adopting a single approach.

124. In engaging with providers, authorities need to have an overview of the impact of their significant purchasing power on the market. The joint strategies they develop with health and housing should acknowledge the effect on service providers. Most authorities do not review systematically whether their purchasing arrangements are developing the market in a positive way.

125. In 1993, at the beginning of the community care reforms, social security rates determined market prices. Social services departments now dominate the market, but they continue to set prices for providers of residential and nursing care close to the prices set by social security rates, rather than to seek the best price for the job that they want doing. This fixed approach results in providers having no incentive to offer higher quality services and/or better prices. Some authorities are realising this: for example, Birmingham City Council has developed a star ratings system that allows the authority to reward providers for higher quality care [CASE STUDY 15, overleaf]. Others are paying increments for more dependent cases to avoid 'cherry-picking' of less dependent users by providers. For example, one fieldwork authority pays four prices for different levels of residential care, although this approach must be carefully managed to avoid giving the provider an incentive to trigger frequent reviews, and may not encourage providers to help older people to become more independent.

CASE STUDY 15

Using pricing to improve quality in the residential care market

Birmingham Social Services Department has contracts with 249 homes for older people within the city and a further 429 outside the city. It conducted a full competitive tendering exercise in 1993. After the first year of contracting the council noted that the prices charged by homes varied by over £40 per resident per week. This prompted the question 'what are we getting for our money in the higher priced homes?' and committed it to developing a system that related the price paid to the standard of service delivered. This approach also avoids the risks of using price as the only determinant of a tender. Following extensive negotiations with the independent sector the council agreed an approach that linked price to the standards of care delivered.

Higher and standard band homes, defined by the percentage of care staff with NVQ level 2 training qualifications and the number of care hours on duty per resident per week, were introduced in 1994. The Department also defined threshold values, and homes that could meet the higher standards could justify charging a higher tender price. Evidence of admission and occupancy rates showed that service users preferred higher band homes.

In 1996 the Department faced budget reductions, which forced it to cut the price paid for residential and nursing care. In a desire to maintain quality, it developed a 'star rating' system and added a third standard:

Standard	Nursing homes	Residential homes
1. **Care hours star**	> 29 hours on duty per resident per week	> 19 hours
2. **NVQ level 2 star**	> 50 per cent care staff trained or in training	> 35 per cent care staff trained or in training
3. **Quality assurance star**	Meets Department's detailed spec, independently verified	As for residential care

All three stars are optional, and for each a higher tender price can be accepted. However, competition means that some three-star homes charge a lower price than some one-star homes. To stimulate the competition, homes are published in all lists in rank order, first by the number of stars, then by price, then by the amount of extra 'top-up' fee charged to the resident. This produces a 'best value' ranking that encourages homes to try to get to the top by offering higher quality at lower prices. The Department's own homes are included in the star rating exercise, but not the tender.

CASE STUDY 15 *(cont.)*

A designated compliance officer manages the system through quarterly returns that are signed by individual staff. Failure to comply leads to price reductions and loss of the star rating. A contract with an accrediting organisation ensures independent verification that the quality assurance (QA) system meets the Department's specification.

The project evolved over two years, but the star rating-system was developed in one year by the contracts officer with IT experience. One-full time post manages the compliance issues, with the external contract for QA verification costing £30,000 a year. The impact on NVQ take-up has been dramatic, seeing a 400 per cent increase. Care hours on duty have increased form 13 to 16 hours per resident. Service users continue to show a preference for higher star rated homes, with three-star rating homes nearly twice as popular as zero-star homes. Combined with the tendering exercise, the Department has actually saved £0.6 million in the first year.

126. The price set by the Department of Social Security for independent sector residential care is £230 per resident per week for shared accommodation and £243 for a single room. Although this price represents only a higher rate of income support, and may not reflect the cost to providers, it is often used as a benchmark. Some authorities have been successful in bringing the unit costs of their own services in line with this benchmark. But many have not, and there is a wide variation that should be addressed [**EXHIBIT 37**].

EXHIBIT 37

Range of unit costs in local authority-provided elderly residential care, 1996/97

The weekly cost varied by a factor of two (excluding the high outlier).

Gross cost per resident week

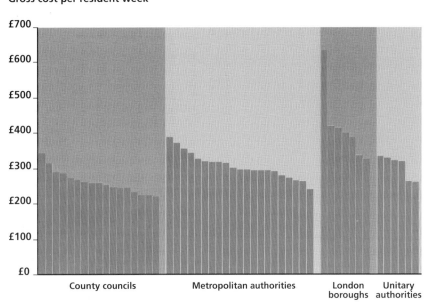

Source: Audit Commission survey

One fieldwork authority ... developed three key measures of quality, based on a survey of users of services.

127. It is not clear that this variation relates to differences in quality. The Personal Social Services Research Unit (PSSRU) reviewed 17 residential homes using 100 quality indicators, including measures devised by health and social care professionals, users and carers (Ref. 31). A major conclusion was that 'homes which performed better on our indicators did not have significantly higher overall costs than those which performed less well'. This suggests that there is scope for purchasers to get better value for money from some providers.

128. In the provision of other services, too, purchasers should try to gain a better understanding of quality. For example, few authorities were able to supply information on how often service providers achieved standards. One fieldwork authority had decided that this was unacceptable and developed three key measures of quality, based on a survey of users of services. They were:

- punctuality of care staff;
- continuity of care worker (numbers of staff and changes in staffing); and
- reliability (how often the care worker failed to turn up at all).

Such measures are a useful start, and enable purchasers and providers to have a common understanding of how to assess quality.

129. As well as pricing, authorities can use thresholds to restrict access on quality grounds, such as approved lists or accreditation. However, most authorities with such lists are not using them to limit access to providers, and very few providers are being turned down. In some cases the process is very simple; in others it is very lengthy and involves supplying the authority with detailed information. Authorities should attempt to avoid placing overly onerous burdens on providers when there is no guarantee of business.

RECOMMENDATION

Social services departments should develop their contracting and funding mechanisms to balance better security to providers with more favourable terms for themselves. In particular, they should broaden the range of contract types and explore ways of achieving better value by rewarding providers for quality and innovation.

Working relationships

130. In all fieldwork authorities, staff complained about the costs of contracting with the independent sector and feared that this made them less efficient than when working with a local authority provider. The Commission found examples of specifications and contracts which together totalled 80 pages. Processes and inputs were sometimes so detailed that it would be very difficult to monitor them effectively. However, no authority had attempted to work out its transaction costs.

131. Inefficient purchasing arrangements are likely to increase transaction costs. The almost universal reliance on spot contracts, with invoices paid to providers on a weekly basis, is likely to cause administrative burdens. A recent survey of 37 authorities by the Audit Commission and Association of Financial Assessment Officers found that the processing inside some authorities could be complex:

- only 19 per cent of respondent authorities used pro forma invoices;
- 36 per cent paid providers by cheque; and
- the number of payments made to home care providers varied widely, but averaged 250 per provider (or 15,000 per authority in one year).

132. There is clearly potential for more efficient processing. For example, one fieldwork authority had worked with a major home care provider to standardise invoicing. It now processes a single form, where previously there were almost 100. As a result, average transaction processing time has dropped from three days to three hours. Such options become easier to create as authorities get to know and trust their providers.

133. Purchasers need to be more open with providers. They could demonstrate their commitment to the relationship by developing key indicators of how well they are enabling providers to serve users. These might include the length and complexity of contract documents, the proportion of expenditure in block contracts, the average number of days notice given to providers before a service is required, records of choices made by service users and the average length of time for payment to take place. Surveys of providers could also be used to test their effectiveness as purchasers.

...some authorities ... focus their partnerships on a select number of proven providers.

134. In practice it is difficult for authorities to work closely with all their providers due to the large numbers of suppliers involved. Authorities visited by the Audit Commission were using between 80 to 1,180 residential and nursing homes. The home care market generally has fewer providers, but even here the numbers can be large: one authority that has a deliberate policy of developing small, local providers found itself having to manage relationships with 130 providers. However, some authorities are beginning to recognise the need to focus their partnerships on a select number of proven providers [CASE STUDIES 16, 17].

CASE STUDY 16

Making room for partnerships in the home care market

Hertfordshire Social Services Department spends around £12 million a year on independent sector home care. It recognised that its current spot contracting arrangements were inappropriate for such a large volume of service, and created unhelpful complexity. In response, it has been progressively expanding the proportion of expenditure under block contracts to cover £4 million in total. The block contracts aim to:

- reduce the administrative and transaction costs of dealing with a large number of providers;

- facilitate the improved evaluation and monitoring of standards;

- reduce service costs if business is transferred on to block contracts. The authority estimated that block contracting could save it £300,000 (2.5 per cent of independent sector home care expenditure), based on the business that it had with its 19 most expensive providers; and

- reduce the risks to service users of service interruption resulting from business failure of small providers.

Hertfordshire's approach has been to develop 14 block contracts ranging from 5,000 hours per year to one county-wide contract for over 130,000 hours. The intention of the smaller blocks is to help to encourage smaller providers to develop by giving them some security of income. These providers can, of course, also provide further hours on a spot-purchase basis, according to the pattern of demand and their capacity.

The largest contract is county-wide and is viewed as more of a partnership, offering:

- a benchmark with which to compare local authority services;

- a reduction in 'transaction' costs, both financial and administrative; and

- lower unit prices.

CASE STUDY 17

Developing new services with the independent sector

In 1994 a borough-wide review of needs for community care in Wandsworth Social Services Department identified that older people from racial minorities were under-represented within the users of social services. This under-representation was due both to a low level of awareness in these communities of the services available and a lack of ethnically sensitive services. The health and social services authorities commissioned research which confirmed that existing services were not adequately meeting needs, but showed that a range of voluntary organisations had experience and expertise in providing services for this group. However, these organisations would be unlikely to meet approved list standards as yet.

The Department therefore funded a three-year development project to develop these providers to work with the authority's care managers. The specific aims were:

- to develop elderly racial minority providers with a view to ultimately reaching the approved list;
- to increase the number of racial minority older people coming forward for community care assessments; and
- to encourage the development of ethnically sensitive assessment practices in care management.

Four voluntary organisations were selected and consultants appointed to work with them to provide training and to help them to become more business-like. In the first year a six-month block contract was agreed to give the providers some security of income, although in practice this financial support was needed only for four months as their incomes soon exceeded this level. Training sessions included:

- the community care legislation and its local implementation;
- contracting for community care;

- setting yourself up as a community business;
- financial management;
- home care awareness;
- managing multiple priorities;
- training of care workers;
- building quality into your work; and
- disability awareness training.

Meetings were also organised with care management staff to establish a working relationship and seminars were held to publicise the work of the groups to the community at large.

Care managers value the new providers: they are purchasing the services of these organisations despite hourly rates being generally higher than those of other providers. The outcome of the project has been a steady rise in the proportion of referrals from ethnic groups: 9 per cent in the third quarter of 1994, rising to 13 per cent in the last quarter of 1995.

RECOMMENDATION

Social services should actively seek better relationships with independent sector providers through a better understanding of the provider's point of view.

Monitoring services

135. Effective commissioning is not simply a matter of developing good specifications: regular monitoring is also needed to ensure effective service delivery and to reduce the risk to the service user. But monitoring services presents problems for most social services departments; although it is particularly important in order to protect vulnerable users, it is very difficult because services are provided in a large number of settings.

136. The monitoring mechanisms in place in most authorities tend to:

- place heavy emphasis on service specifications that aim to reduce risk;

- ask care managers to monitor and review regularly, but in practice they find it difficult to make time for this;

- designate 'client-side' monitoring officers for contracts (although this is often one officer for hundreds of contracts); and

- operate a complaints procedure.

137. While these measures represent a start, the perception by providers is of a fragmented approach with some duplication. For example, the work of the registration and inspection unit is often duplicated in part by contract compliance work. In addition, over-reliance on reactive mechanisms, such as complaints procedures, might not work for more vulnerable service users who may be reluctant to complain. More proactive ways of seeking users' views for monitoring purposes are rare.

138. None of the fieldwork authorities systematically collected statistical information across services on quality and outcomes for the purposes of central monitoring. Authorities address quality and outcomes in the care specification, but in a way that is open to interpretation and not measurable. Even where monitoring is taking place, the information is not captured in a useful way.

139. Another concern is that the monitoring arrangements focus almost exclusively on the external providers. In only two (out of twelve) fieldwork authorities are the arrangements the same for local authority and independent sector providers. While many authorities argue that local authority providers have their own internal checks, they are still not subject to the same scrutiny as external providers, and as a result those who use local authority services are potentially less well protected. This approach also damages any attempt to be transparent and even-handed with external providers.

What is needed is a cohesive approach to quality that brings together all those involved in the care process

140. No system will eliminate all risk, but the resources that most authorities can make available for monitoring are scant. Authorities without watertight monitoring arrangements risk failures of quality, which could be as serious as abuse or neglect of vulnerable service users. They therefore need to make full use of the resources that they do have, within a cohesive approach to quality that brings together all those involved in the care process [EXHIBIT 38].

EXHIBIT 38

Potential elements of a monitoring approach

The respective roles need to be worked out to avoid duplication and to minimise risk.

CARE MANAGERS?

INSPECTION AND REGISTRATION?

PROVIDERS?

CENTRAL CONTRACTS?

COMPLAINTS PROCESS?

ADVOCATES?

DEFINING STANDARDS?

USERS AND CARERS?

TRAINING OF STAFF?

Source: Audit Commission

141. However, the greatest safeguard is likely to be achieved by encouraging service providers to conduct self-assessment procedures and monitor and improve their own services. Over-reliance on spot purchasing makes monitoring more complex, too. Those authorities which have used block or cost-and-volume purchasing have found that it creates an opportunity to ask providers to take on self-monitoring [CASE STUDY 19, overleaf]. But such a step requires a strong partnership in which the commissioner trusts the provider (and vice versa). Such trust grows gradually as each gets to know the other.

CASE STUDY 19

A 'risk assessment' approach to monitoring

Westminster Social Services Department has introduced a 'risk-assessment' framework to tailor the monitoring of care to the requirements of the individual. The aim is to avoid over-monitoring or under-monitoring for the level of risk.

The framework enables care managers to establish for each client:

• an up-front agreement with providers of who will do what; and

• any monitoring required from the two council-wide monitoring officers.

It has also drawn on two related projects :

• selection of providers for block contracts – when tendering for contracts they evaluate the provider's ability to reduce the risk to the service user through its own self-monitoring. One large home care provider has a 24-hour 'complaints hotline' and actively encourages service users to phone and complain; and

• empowering users through the 'Westminster Guarantee', which sets standards that users can expect from services, based on a survey of what users say they want from services.

RECOMMENDATION

Social services departments should develop more watertight monitoring arrangements to ensure effective and high quality service delivery, co-ordinating the resources that they have and adding to them where necessary.

Conclusion

142. Health and social services need to improve their information base for commissioning services and this should enable them to encourage providers to develop a complementary range of services. However, good relationships with providers are also key to a better understanding of the provider's point of view by purchasers.

RECOMMENDATIONS

3 Rebalancing Services

Mapping needs and services

1 Health authorities and social services departments must map needs and the services available to meet them. They should share this information with each other as the basis for joint planning and commissioning.

2 Health authorities and trusts should review whether older people are currently being admitted to hospital beds because alternative services are not available and identify what alternative services are needed.

3 Social services should review their spending patterns, use of residential and nursing homes, use of home care and any limits to placements, and make adjustments in this mix where needed.

Strengthening management information

4 Health and social services authorities should support their mapping processes by introducing information systems that allow them to update their maps on a regular basis.

Working with service providers

5 Health authorities should work with trusts to develop new forms of provision to reduce admissions to hospital by providing care in alternative ways, and explore ways of improving rehabilitation after treatment where appropriate.

6 Social services should actively seek better relationships with independent sector providers through a better understanding of the provider's point of view.

7 Social services should develop their contracting and funding mechanisms to improve the balance between security for providers and more favourable terms for themselves. In particular, they should explore ways of rewarding providers for quality and innovation.

Assuring quality

8 Social services should develop more watertight monitoring arrangements to ensure effective and high quality service delivery, co-ordinating the resources that they have and adding to them where necessary.

4

The Way Forward

Improving the efficiency and effectiveness of care for older people requires short- and medium-term actions at both strategic and operational levels. And the system would benefit further from a national review of policy and funding.

The pressures to provide good services for older people are likely to continue to grow...

143. The pressures to provide good services for older people are likely to continue to grow as the numbers of older people increase over the coming years, and as expectations rise. This report has identified approaches that authorities and trusts are already introducing to make improvments. But more could be done. Fortunately, not everything needs to be done at once and the slowing down of the growth rate in the numbers of older people gives an opportunity to start a programme that will deliver the necessary changes. Nevertheless, pressures are growing now and many hospitals face a difficult winter ahead. The Department of Health has already indicated that the first steps need to be taken quickly. The actions proposed in this report have therefore been categorised as either:

- short-term actions – which should be taken immediately;
- medium-term actions – which should be started as soon as possible, but which are likely to take time to complete; or
- strategic issues – broader questions that must be addressed and may require fundamental changes to current arrangements.

144. So far this report has described actions that fall into the first two of these three categories. They are repeated below, grouped into their respective categories. But these actions on their own will not be enough, and the report ends with some strategic issues for further consideration.

Short-term actions

145. Many authorities are already under considerable pressure. But some actions can be taken immediately to help to manage this problem.

Mapping needs and services

Authorities and trusts need to understand their immediate pressures.

- All health authorities and social services departments must now assess the needs that they face and the services available to meet them. They should share this information with each other as the basis for joint planning and commissioning.
- Health authorities and trusts should review whether older people are currently being admitted to hospital beds because alternative services are not available and identify what alternative services are needed to take the pressure off acute and social services.
- Social services should review their capacity to respond to demands from health – their use of residential and nursing homes, use of home care and any limits to placements – and discuss difficulties and possible options with health colleagues.

Managing discharge

Health trusts and social services need to streamline discharge arrangements.

- Health trusts and social services staff should agree on their respective responsibilities for different stages of the discharge process.

- Together they should undertake an audit of all alleged discharge delays and identify who is responsible.

- Social services staff should agree time standards with health trusts (and with health authorities as necessary) for key milestones to the implementation of a care package.

- Trusts should make an officer responsible for monitoring discharge delays on a regular basis, identifying who is responsible and checking time standards, and reporting to the trust chief executive and director of social services.

- Health trusts and social services staff should review assessment arrangements, clarifying responsibilities for different members of staff, standardising procedures and documentation and monitoring the completion of documentation. They should consider introducing panels to monitor proposed placements in residential and nursing homes.

Strengthening care management

Social services should ensure that care management is efficient and responsive.

- Social services should ensure that users are fully informed and involved in the care management process by providing information about the process, about the full range of choices available (in the form of directories), ways of complaining and of changing services where necessary. They should consider the use of advocacy for older people.

- Social services should undertake a systematic review of packages of home care where this has not been done recently.

Medium-term actions

146. All of the above actions are needed urgently. The medium-term changes are no less important, but they are likely to require more time for development and implementation. They address the problems described in the vicious circle [EXHIBIT 32, p51] and help authorities to break out of this circle through joint planning and commissioning of services.

Strengthening management information

Authorities should ensure that mapping becomes routine practice.

- Health and social services authorities should support their mapping processes by introducing information systems that allow them to update their maps on a regular basis.

Working with service providers

Authorities should strengthen links with providers.

- Health authorities should work with trusts to develop new forms of provision to reduce admissions to hospital by providing care in alternative ways, and explore ways of improving rehabilitation after treatment where appropriate.

- Social services should actively seek better relationships with independent sector providers through a better understanding of the provider's point of view.

- Social services should develop their contracting and funding mechanisms to improve the balance between security for providers and more favourable terms for themselves. In particular, they should explore ways of rewarding providers for quality and innovation.

Assuring quality

Social services should develop their capacity to monitor service delivery.

- Social services should develop more watertight monitoring arrangements to ensure effective and high quality service delivery, co-ordinating the resources that they have and adding to them where necessary.

Strengthening care management

Social services should continue to develop care management practices.

- Social services should develop care managers' influence over services by reducing restrictions on choice, introducing service-level agreements with in-house providers and at least delegating budgets to teams, providing the necessary financial controls and advice are in place. Authorities should ensure that unit costs of in-house services are calculated and made available to care managers.

- Social services should ensure that procedures are in place to review services regularly to check that care plans are being achieved and that resources are being used to best effect.

Strategic issues

147. There is much that authorities can do for themselves to improve arrangements locally, and the case studies in the report reflect the wide range of initiatives that authorities are already taking. But local agencies are still constrained by the policy framework within which they are asked to operate and may be inhibited from achieving best value as a result.

148. The most recent major national strategic document concerned solely with older people was the 1981 White Paper, *'Growing Older'*, now 16 years old. Since then, services for older people have been driven by individual policy initiatives – such as efficiency pressures on acute care, policies for community care or guidance on continuing care – that have not added up to a coherent strategy overall. Some developments have actually run counter to stated policy – for example, increased use of homes and reducing use of home care in some authorities – and some have never been stated as policy – such as the steady reduction of long-term NHS beds. As a result, older people's needs are not being fully considered, and instead of benefiting from well co-ordinated services they have become labelled 'bed blockers'.

149. A coherent framework is needed that addresses the following issues:

- the roles and responsibilities of the respective agencies; and
- the level of funding required to discharge the role, and the source of that funding.

Clarity of roles and responsibilities

150. This report has described the increasing withdrawal of the NHS as a provider of long-term care and the growth of the independent sector to fill the gap left by the NHS. This development has left social services in a position where they have had to follow the NHS rather than set their own priorities and pursue, for example, a more preventative agenda. While local initiatives should not be constrained, some may require a clear statement of policy from government. This might include answers to the following questions:

- Where should the boundaries of responsibility lie between the NHS, social services, housing and other agencies?
- What is the role of the NHS in long-term care?
- Should national standards be set for care and, and if so, how should these be implemented, funded and measured?
- What is the correct balance between acute and preventative and rehabilitative services?
- Should direct payments be extended to older people to strengthen the user's influence? If so, what does this mean for the role of social services?
- Are new arrangements required to develop care management skills further?

Removing these constraints would enhance the potential for joint investment...

151. In addressing these questions actions can be taken that facilitate change. For example, restrictions on how health and social services spend their funds make the pooling of budgets difficult. Health can pass funds to social services, but these cannot then be spent on healthcare; social services cannot pass money to health or set up a third agency to act jointly on their behalf. Removing these constraints would enhance the potential for joint investment, once joint priorities have been agreed.

Funding of long-term care

152. It is impossible to determine with certainty how much funding will be required for community care. Much depends on the standards and range of services expected by older people and how far society will go to meet these expectations. The adequacy of the funding for long-term care needs to be reviewed both now and for the future. There is time to anticipate the next increase in the proportion of elderly people in the next century, and planning must start soon.

153. Such a review might address the issue of how far the state has a responsibility to support individuals, and how far individuals should plan for their own needs. At present each generation pays for the previous one through taxation. This may no longer be sustainable as the proportion of economically active people shrinks over the next 40 to 50 years and the number of people over 75 and 85 grows. Given the review of pension provision underway at present, it may be appropriate to consider ways of funding long-term care at the same time and fund both in a similar way.

154. The debate about funding needs to take place alongside the development of a comprehensive national strategy that ensures that the funds facilitate good quality local health and social services for older people – based upon the needs of older people in the new millennium and not on the series of reactive policy developments of the last 15 years.

155. The development of such a co-ordinated framework for the care of older people, together with guidance on local service configuration, would help to ensure that resources are utilised efficiently and provide the quality of care that older people need.

Appendix 1

Checklist for action

	Health authorities	Health trusts	Social services departments	Central government
SHORT-TERM ACTIONS				
Understand the immediate pressures...				
Map needs and services and share this information with other agencies as the basis for joint planning and commissioning	✓	✓	✓	
Review use of acute beds by older people; identify possible alternative services	✓	✓		
Review social services' capacity to respond to changes in health service provision	✓		✓	
Streamline discharge arrangements...				
Agree discharge responsibilities and time standards; audit all alleged discharge delays and identify who is responsible		✓	✓	
Make an officer responsible for monitoring discharge, reporting to the chief executive and director of social services		✓		
Review assessment arrangements and consider use of multidisciplinary panels		✓	✓	
Ensure that care management is effective...				
Ensure that older people are fully involved in care planning and aware of the choices available. Consider use of advocacy for older people			✓	
Review allocation of home care packages where this has not been done recently			✓	
MEDIUM-TERM ACTIONS				
Ensure that mapping becomes routine...				
Develop information systems to support the mapping process and update the maps	✓		✓	
Strengthen links with service providers...				
Work together to develop alternative services for older people. In particular, explore ways of improving rehabilitation after treatment	✓	✓		
Seek better relationships with independent providers			✓	
Review contracting and funding mechanisms to encourage quality and innovation			✓	
Develop monitoring capacity...				
Improve the co-ordination and coverage of the monitoring process			✓	
Continue to develop care management...				
Develop care management's influence over services, introducing service level agreements with in-house providers, making unit costs available and pursuing financial devolvement			✓	
Ensure that all services are reviewed regularly to ensure effective targeting			✓	
STRATEGIC ACTIONS				
Provide a coherent and helpful framework...				
Clarify the roles and responsibilities of the NHS and social services in long-term care and the level of funding required to match these				✓
Encourage greater emphasis on prevention and rehabilitation				✓
Encourage development of care management skills				✓

Appendix 2

Members of the Advisory Group

Continuing Care

Lorna Easterbrook	Age Concern
Nicola Ford	Community Physiotherapy, Burlingbroke Hospital
Adrienne Fresko	Audit Commissioner
Dr Rowan Harwood	Queens Medical Centre, Nottingham
Dr Tim Hill	General Practitioner
John James	Chief Executive, Kensington, Chelsea and Westminster Health Authority
Professor David Jolley	Medical Director, Penn Hospital, Wolverhampton
Jim Kennedy	Social Services Inspectorate, Department of Health
Rosalynde Lowe	Audit Commissioner
Professor Peter Millard	St George's Hospital Medical School
Professor Elaine Murphy	Chairman, City and Hackney Community Services NHS Trust
Nicky Pendleton	General Manager, Queen Alexandra Hospital, Portsmouth
Jill Pitkeathly	Carers National Association
Dr Anita Thomas	Consultant Geriatrician
Helena Shovelton	Audit Commissioner
Professor Gerald Wistow	Nuffield Institute for Health

Commissioning Community Care

Terry Bamford	Director of Housing and Social Services, Royal Borough of Kensington and Chelsea (Association of Metropolitan Authorities and County Councils)
Jules Forder	Personal Social Services Research Unit
John Foster	Audit Commissioner
Tessa Harding	Help the Aged
Nigel Jones	Nuffield Institute for Health
Lucianne Sawyer	United Kingdom Home Care Association
Sheila Scott	National Care Homes Association
Jonathan Stopes-Roe	Department of Health
Raymond Warburton	Department of Health
Sir Ron Watson	Audit Commissioner
Andrew Webster	Joint Reviews of Social Services
Katherine Wright	Department of Health

Members of both Advisory Groups

Ian Plaister	NHS Executive
Mary Richardson	Director of Social Services, London Borough of Waltham Forest (Association of Directors of Social Services)

References

1. OPCS *Sub-national Population Projections (England)*, Series PP3 No. 9, Government Statistical Service, HMSO, 1995. `

2. Centre for Health Services Research, *Pathways Through Care: A Study of the Processes and Outcomes of Hospital Care for Older People: Executive Summary*, University of Newcastle Upon Tyne, 1996, drawing on J Bond and D Buck, *Comparative Study of Social Protection for Dependency in Old Age in the United Kingdom*, University of Newcastle upon Tyne, 1994.

3. CIPFA, *1995/96 Actuals: Local Authorities in England and Wales*, CIPFA, 1996.

4. Audit Commission, *Lying in Wait*, HMSO, 1992.

5. Audit Commission, *Making a Reality of Community Care*, HMSO, 1986.

6. Laing & Buisson, *Care of Elderly People Market Survey*, Laing & Buisson Publications Ltd, 1997.

7. G Wistow, '*The Changing Scene in Britain*' in T Harding, B Meredith, and G Wistow, *Options for Long Term Care*, HMSO, 1996.

8. G Wistow, 'Increasing Private Provision of Social Care: Implications of Policy' in B Lewis, *Care and Control: Personal Social Services and the Private Sector*, Discussion Paper 15, Policy Studies Institute, 1987.

9. House of Commons Health Committee, *Memorandum from the Department of Health on Public Expenditure on Health and the Personal Social Services*, First Special Report, Session 1993–1994, HC 617, HMSO, 1994.

10. House of Commons Health Committee, *Long-Term Care: NHS Responsibilities for Meeting Continuing Health Care Needs*, First Report, Session 1995-1996, HC 19-1, HMSO, 1995.

11. House of Commons Health Committee, *Long-Term Care: Future Provision and Funding*, Third Report, Session 1995-1996, HC 59-1, HMSO, 1996.

12. Department of Health, *NHS Responsibilities For Meeting Continuing Health Care Needs*, HSG (95) 8, Department of Health, 1995.

13. Department of Health Finance Department.

14. M Bennet, E Smith, P Millard, *The Right Person? The Right Place? The Right Time? An Audit of the Appropriateness of Nursing Home Placements Post Community Care Act*, Department of Geriatric Medicine, St George's Hospital Medical School, 1995.

15. L Kalra, Evaluation of the Intensive Continuing Care Resource Project, King's College London, St George's Hospital Medical School, 1996.

16. D Challis, R Darton, L Johnson, M Stone, K Traske, *Care Management and Health Care of Older People*, Arena/PSSRU University of Kent, 1995.

17. *Reviewing Social Services: Annual Report* 1997, Social Services Inspectorate and Audit Commission, Joint Reviews, 1997.

18. G Zarb, *Cashing In On Independence – Comparing the Costs and Benefits of Cash and Services*, British Council of Organisations of Disabled People, 1994.

19. *Community Care Statistics*, 1996 (England), Department of Health, April 1997.

20. Audit Commission, *United They Stand*, Audit Commission/HMSO, 1995.

21. P Gertman and J Restuccia, 'The Appropriateness Evaluation Protocol: A Technique for Assessing Unnecessary Days of Hospital Care', *Medical Care 19* (8), 1981, pp855–71.

22. P Tsang and M Severs, 'A Study of Appropriateness of Acute Geriatric Admissions and an Assessment of the Appropriateness Evaluation Protocol', *Journal of the Royal College of Physicians of London, 29 (4)*, 1995, pp311–14.

23. *Mid 1993 Population Estimates for England and Wales*, HMSO, 1994; *Mid 1996 Population Estimates for England and Wales*, HMSO, 1997; ONS, *Economic Trends: Annual Supplement*, HMSO, 1996/97.

24. Audit Commission, *Balancing the Care Equation*, Audit Commission HMSO, 1996.

25. *Income Support Statistics – Quarterly Enquiry: Residential and Nursing Home Care Report*, Department of Social Security, May 1996; *Residential Accommodation, Detailed Statistics on Residential Care Homes and Local Authority Supported Residents, England, 1996*, Department of Health, 1997.

26. *Community Care Statistics: Detailed Statistics on Local Authority Personal Social Services for Adults, England, 1994, 1995, 1996*, Department of Health, 1995, 1996 and 1997.

27. Association of Metropolitan Authorities and the Association of County Councils, *Who Gets Community Care: A Survey of Community Care Eligibility Criteria*, AMA, 1995.

28. D Black and C Bowman, 'Community Institutional Care for Frail Elderly People – Time to Structure Professional Responsibility', *British Medical Journal*, Vol. 315, 23 August, 1997, pp441–2.

29. LGMB, *Community Care Trends* 1997 Report, LGMB, 1997.

30. *The Connected Corporation*, Jordan D Lewis, Free Press, 1995.

31. J Schneider, A Mann, A Netten, 'Residential Care for Elderly People: An Exploratory Study of Quality Measurement', *Mental Health Research Review* 4, April 1997, pp12–15.

Index References are to paragraph numbers, Boxes and Case Studies